In the Silence of this Room

International authors share their thoughts
in poetry and prose, linked by
global issues that haunt us all.

In the Silence of this Room

International authors share their thoughts
in poetry and prose, linked by
global issues that haunt us all.

Edited by Diane Smith

Globe
Alex Braverman

In the Silence of this Room

Editor: Diane Smith

Limited First Edition Published

November 1st, 2009

ISBN: 978-0-615-28002-8

Grey Sparrow Press
St. Paul, Minnesota

In Memoriam

Elsie (Stanwood) O'Day
passed away June 17th, 2009
from a massive heart attack.

She was a bright spirit;
feisty, strong, talented, and kind.

Ms. O'Day wrote with us for
two consecutive years and
offered poems of light, hope,
and charm.

May she rest in peace.

DEDICATED

To My Beloved Family,
Randall and Ralph

And the International Writers
and Photographers Who Made
this Book Possible.

Writers and Photographers

Nick Bakshi
Sita Bhaskar
Alex Braverman
A. Jefferson Brown
Raguel Chalfi, [Translator: Tsipi Keller]
L. McKenna Donovan
Marie Lynam Fitzpatrick
Marko Fong
Cleveland W. Gibson
Hannatu Green
Jeff Haas
Sue Haigh
Robert Hampton
Alamgir Hashmi
Kyle Hemmings
Frank J. Hutton
Shanna Karella
Katherine Elizabeth Kennedy
Tiffany Larsen
Dean Lawson
Kulvinder Singh Matharu
Elsie (Stanwood) O'Day
James S. Oppenheim
Ajay Prasannan
Ivan Gabriel Rehorek
Bill Frank Robinson
Randy Ulland
Townsend Walker
Ann Walters
Mike Woof
Neng Xiong

In Gratitude

To Film Director Francis Ford Coppola
and his staff for the creation of Zoetrope:
an online writing venue for new writers
and emerging authors.

To all the contributing writers and photographers
for their time, wisdom, and patience.

With deep appreciation and thanks to
Townsend Walker, Sue Haigh, Kyle Hemmings,
Bill Jones, and Frank J. Hutton for their
countless hours of help and support.

To Andrew McIntosh Patrick
and his sister, Ann Patrick, for their
kind permission to reproduce
A City Garden.

—Diane Smith

Seth Eastman, Oil, 1870-1875

Introduction
Diane Smith, Editor

THE MISSISSIPPI RIVER CARRIES ME BACK to younger days when I catch butterflies and fish for trout. This day we go swimming by the dam—yes, I am twelve.

Beth, my friend, has long flowing black hair and wears a low-slung, pink-checkered bikini. I'm wearing a light blue one, not as steamy. The tiny dam is appealing—jumping off the cement reservoir with the fast current below. The swirling water drags our bodies towards the grating. Bravely, I counter-balance the pressure, pulling free, again and again, rising to the surface. None of us tire of this dance, immortality rests on our shoulders. The sun is searing and warms the rippled water on the surface to a tepid tea. My brother joins us; splashing, screaming, laughing wildly. We're all friends and share our intimate secrets.

Dad finds us by the dam to call us in for dinner and yells, "Get out of there. How many times have I told you not to swim by the dam?"

"We're okay," I say.

"Yeah," David says. "Why do you worry about this place?"

"Out, now," Dad yells. "It's not safe. I don't want you swimming here again. Mom has dinner. Come on, time to go."

I grab the cement edge that juts above the water, hoisting myself up with disappointment, feeling the hot cement beneath as I sit down on the edge of the dam catching my breath. My brother and Beth follow, sitting down next to me.

"One last jump," Beth stands and winks.

"No, no more. Time to come in," Dad insists again.

Slender, with wet hair glistening in the sun, Beth draws her two hands above her head pressing them together, performing a dive that soundlessly breaks the glass. I wait for her head to bob up. I wait and I wait. Then, Dad's abrupt movements distract my eyes. He runs and jumps in the water, yes, he runs, and disappears below the surface. Now, my brother runs and jumps in too. I race around the small bridge and enter the silvery liquid from the shore. My brother is already well below the surface. I move in quickly. All of us, legs flailing, search. The water is cooler a few feet below, pristine, sunlight streaming though, diminishing into the depths. Specks of algae sift through eddies. The seaweed is buffeted back and forth. I can't find Beth. I can't see Daddy or David. Need air, I think, need air now, must get to the surface. Seaweed brushes my face, terrifying me, forcing me to close my eyes.

I rise, gulping air and dive deep again, shaking. The pull of the current towards the grating is strong. It's easy to stay below the surface now, as I edge towards the forbidden, yet familiar steel poles. It's why I always stay away from the metal grating. The current will overpower me.

Then, I realize; Beth is frantic, strung across several poles. Her eyes meet mine, head shaking; bubbles escape her lips and rise to the surface. Her long hair is tangled around one of them.

Daddy is fighting the current, pulling at the wrapped strands. Finally, with one hard tug, he yanks her free. I watch him fight the current and pull her by the arm to air.

All our heads pop up together. Beth is still conscious. She is gasping, coughing as Daddy guides her from the water's edge. She starts shaking violently as he grabs a towel and places it round her shoulders.

At this moment, I know I have witnessed Beth's dance of death. I have also witnessed Daddy's dance of life; the dance of my danseur noble.

In the silence of this room, I remember my childhood and my father that day. I feel a sense of urgency, a need to say something. My greatest concern is that war is everywhere.

I invite a few writers to develop a project with me—to speak to issues and worries we all share. They write bravely of a better home for all the citizens of the world, writers from every continent and every faith. Like my father, they are my heroes.

Trees cast long shadows as the afternoon slips away. My father's lesson comes back to me. Take care of the living first.

Upstate New York
Ralph Smith

Tibet
Randy Ulland

Table of Contents

Introduction
Diane Smith, Editor

"Les qualités acquises et qui se développent
lentement en nous sont les liens invisibles
qui rattachent chacun de nos
existers l'un à l'autre..."

"The virtues we acquire,
which develop slowly within us,
are the invisible links that bind
our existence to those of others..."

[Translator Sue Haigh]

Le Livre Mystique, II, par Honoré de Balzac
Séraphîta, 315, (Extrait des Études Philosophiques)
Paris. Werdet, Libraire-Éditeur,

1er décembre 1835

Chapter One
How Beautiful upon the Hills

A Tiger's Hand
Ann Walters

"Last few days I had a sort of feeling, a tiger,
of a young deer in a tiger's hand."
—His Holiness, the Dalai Lama

Like lifting weights or calling home
after fifty-three years. Hard.

Impotence is advertised on every
late-night channel but has not been

truly understood until now.
In the season of rebirth

soldiers spring from the ground
like an army of Athenas, fully formed

and ready to assimilate the violence of lust,
of wanting what is not theirs.

What is not theirs is the heart, working
at eighty-three beats per minute to put

perspective in every home. Home has
never been so distant, it seems,

so wholly accessible from far away.
The arm stretches, the claws extend.

Snow melting on the tiger's hand leaves no mark,
only a drop of water shaped like a tear.

Tibet
Randy Ulland

Tel Aviv

Boats in the Harbor

On the Shore, Tel Aviv, Winter 1974

Raquel Chalfi [Translator Tsipi Keller]

A crocodile cloud swallowed a cloud-cloud.
All is clogged
and where did the war go?
The pier is painted red and yellow
with the inscription: Tel Aviv.
The drums of the depths are indifferent.
In the sky shadowy figures
frolic unhurriedly. The infinite wrestling arena
in slow-motion takes.
A crane rises above the luxury hotel
Hilton. And where did the war go.
A crocodile cloud swallowed a cloud-cloud. Where
did the war go. Up   in the depths
soft clouds make love to planes.
The air fills the lungs
with spiky salt and laughter.
The sun, a fading photograph.
Birds on the shore greyly peck the sand.
The sea—its muscles groan.
A lone woman, a synthetic kerchief
on her head   what is she
in face of a thunderstorm.
The diving board, too, is painted orange.

An old woman, her lips attempt:

> He was an angel
> He was an angel

Tibet
Randy Ulland

The Mekong River, *Kulvinder Singh Matharu*

Land of a Million Elephants
Oral Testimony, Neng Xiong

LAOS IS BLESSED with the Mekong River, green-misted mountains, bamboo, and *dok champa* flowers of every color. Crocodiles, flamingos and water buffalo roam the River. Elephants used to run wild. Now, they live only in the city. I grew up in this world on a small Hmong farm. My life was as rare and lovely as the wild orchids that flourished in the Laos forests.

Our land was invaded in 1961 and war came. The Hmong fought hard, trying to help Americans push the invaders out, but failed. My people were forced into exile after the War; those who survived.

I remember well that day on the Mekong River, the day we fled. I was pregnant with my first child. Clouds of fire and smoke filled the sky. Villagers strapped bamboo or banana branches to their bodies so they would float with the current to the other side, others paddled in bamboo boats. Bombs screeched over our heads with volleys of gunfire. We heard little children and babies crying, their voices rising above the loud explosions.

My brother-in-law, sister-in-law and their six children were the last to leave our farm. We searched for them, paddling fast. I looked back and saw them in the distance. I turned to my husband and screamed so he could hear me through the loudness of the air, "They are coming, they are …" I looked back a second time. My brother-in-law and his family were gone.

Soldiers with machine guns dropped villagers in the River in seconds. Heads, necks, arms were severed and tossed through the air like bloodied tree limbs in typhoons. The Mekong River was so filled with Hmong bodies, no space could be seen between them. So much blood from my people and my family. My village burned.

My husband and I made it to the Thai refugee camp. Later, we met my sister-in-law there. She did not talk at first. As time passed, she explained all her children were killed- her husband too. We already knew this. To think she survived. She said a Thai boat picked her up in the water and brought her to the shore. She walked two miles to the Camp. We all stayed there through several months of despair and eventually received visas to come to the United States.

Neng and her family in Mailoua, Laos.

I have lived in the United States many years now. I want you to know, I am proud to be an American citizen. I am safe here. Many of my beautiful children were born in America. My children are educated. We have enough food to eat and people help us.

A while ago, I lost my husband to leukemia. When I am troubled, I set a place for him at our table and fill his plate with fresh steaming vegetables and sticky rice, with a large piece of rich pork. I ask him for help, to help me understand.

A Brief Love

Raquel Chalfi [Translator Tsipi Keller]

Slices slices silence has cut
through us

He took me from the noise
and time became a summer of grace
between killings
and I reached my hand   and he came like a rain of grace

and on Mount Zion the darkness was thick
and the little light in the churchyard was frail   frail
and I reached my hand   and he fell into me in despair despair
and later he led me by the hand
like the sighted leads the blind
and we saw so much so much
it was possible to touch the roots of things
and we saw until our eyes refused to retain
two beautiful weeks
between wars
do you know what it means two full innocent weeks
between death and death
you can't ask for more than that and if we were to ask
it would have had a measure of arrogance

It was such a cruel beauty

And such a silence
on the altar

Sonny Udo's Story
Mike Woof

SOON AFTER WE MOVED into our rented house in Uruk Ata where we would be teaching in the local school, our landlord Sonny invited Craig and myself to share a few glasses of *kai kai* with him. We walked across the small yard separating our house from his compound and he greeted us at the door, then ushered us into his front room. There, we settled back in the comfort of his heavy hardwood armchairs and began sipping from the bottle of clear, fiery *kai kai*, a spirit distilled from palm wine, that his wife had poured into small glasses and set out on the low coffee table in front of us. Sonny was always keen to make us welcome and this time as often after, he said, "My home is yours."

After the level in the bottle had dropped by a few centimeters we all became loquacious. I don't know how we got onto the subject of the Biafran War. But given that Biafra's brutal struggle for independence had once been on the front pages of newspapers around the world and that we were in the area where pitched battles had been fought, it was inevitable it would come up in conversation at some point.

Sonny had a lot to say. He was a great talker and told stories with the practiced air of an accomplished speaker who was familiar with his material.

"Civil war is the worst kind of war," he began, "brother fights brother, neighbor fights neighbor, no one win." He paused and drained his glass.

"Dis area, very bad," he carried on, "there are many killings, many dead, some call it genocide. I am just a boy and the Biafran soldiers come to the village to recruit. Some of them I know from Okoyo nearby and they say, 'You are our brother, come with us and fight for your village and your Biafran country like a man,' and because I am just a boy, twelve years, I follow them."

Craig and I looked at each other, both wondering if this was some tall tale as Sonny paused to refill our glasses, then continued, "Dem dey give me a uniform to wear, then a gun to carry and they show me how it works but we have no bullets to waste for practice. The first time I fire it is the first time I kill a man."

There was a conviction in his voice that I hadn't heard before. And he looked straight at us as he paused to refill his glass.

"Dis area, very bad," he said again, "it is Biafra first, then Nigeria takes it, but we Biafrans make a push and take it back, one, two times, before we are beaten."

"One of the teachers at school said the battle for Azumini up the road was one of the worst of the war," Craig said.

"Yes, many people killed," answered Sonny. "My platoon is done finish at Azumini, all except for me. It happen like this. We are trekking through the bush towards the front when the Nigerian army come out from hiding to surprise us and then everyone is firing. They have more guns and more bullets and soon there are few of us left, so we throw down our rifles and surrender, hands over heads, like so (and he demonstrated with his hands). As the Nigerian soldiers take our guns, I see one sergeant is from this place, this village na Uruk Ata. He is a friend of my uncle's but he does not speak or look at me."

"Dey march us from the bush into Azumini but before we get there, the sergeant pulls me to one side and say to the officer, 'Dis na small boy from my village, he never shave yet and he know nothing,' then he give me a shirt and short trouser to wear, tell me to take off my uniform and say, 'Go run for bush. Go to your mother.'"

"I do like he say and run and the Nigerians not follow, though I hear plenty shooting behind. I never see anyone from my platoon again."

"When I get to my house, my mother cry and say, 'Quick, quick, we have to go hide for forest. If the Nigerian soldiers find you, they will know you na for Biafra and kill you,' so my family carry small things and go hide. Plenty other people hide in forest, too, and one woman, she have a baby and it cry. Everyone say, 'It make too much noise, the soldiers go hear and come kill us,' so she take the baby away and leave it and everyone trek long way, to Ukanafun and past."

He continued, "After small time, we stay for my mother's brother at Ukanafun where war already finished and is safer, for one week, two weeks before we return. When we come back, many things thieved from my father's compound, many Uruk Ata people dead and many small babies have been left in forest. Dis na bad time for Nigeria."

Sonny paused at this and I had to ask, "So what happened to the sergeant, the friend of your father, the man who saved you?"

"He lives here in Uruk Ata," He said, "You teach his grandson."

Sonny sighed and said, "Civil war is very bad. It is the worst kind of war."

"And what happened to the babies left in the forest?" Craig asked.

"Some the Nigerian soldiers find and take away to orphanage, and some die," Sonny answered.

Later on, when we'd finished the bottle of *kai kai*, Craig and I said goodnight to Sonny and stumbled across the dusty front yard that lay between the two houses.

"Do you think he was telling the truth?" Craig asked.

"Haven't a clue."

Sonny was a great talker and told this story with the practiced air of an accomplished speaker who was familiar with his material. It was hard to be sure.

It was Craig who met the sergeant a few weeks later and over a beer the story was confirmed ". . . practically word for word."

Starving Nigerian Girl
Nigerian-Biafran Civil War
-Courtesy of
The Centers for Disease Control and Prevention

Ugly Time
Ivan Gabriel Rehorek

I WAS ONLY TEN when the tanks came. I recall skipping downstairs to the main entrance one morning, and seeing the big gate blocked off. The house we lived in at the time was one of those old nineteenth century places, typical for Europe, with the carriageway serving as a main entrance. The horses and buggies had long gone, but the place itself was still standing. And out the front, I could make out a large red star on a dull grey background.

There was a Russian tank stuck halfway down our cul-de-sac, and soldiers were climbing about, shouting at each other.

I sneaked past and ran up the street to school. People were pointing and waving, and there were helicopters blibbing about. School was closed, so I went back home.

The tank was still there and someone was tinkering with the engine, cursing and carrying on a conversation with God.

"Why do you punish me this way, Almighty? Why is this piece of junk still standing? Why is our officer strutting about like a rooster; it's not as if the girls are interested in a peasant like him? Why is this wrench bending, and look at this mess..."

The officer in question was indeed strutting his stuff, but no one was watching. The real performance was in the back of the tank, and it had escalated to a banging and yelling stage. "So you won't work, after all I have done for you! BAAANG!! Ungrateful wretch, how often have I oiled your gears and greased your pistons? BAAAANG!! Well? Nothing to say? BAAANG!!!"

Another voice joined in: "You heap of scrap metal!! CRAAASH!!! Your mother was a broken-down tractor and your father belonged in the Agricultural Museum!!!"

The glorious Red army had indeed come to deliver us from the perils of capitalism, but it appeared as if they were not going to have an easy time of it.

This same army, or at least, the previous generation, years ago were greeted as saviors, after they'd swept back the Nazis like a tide of sewage.

Here in Pilsen, General Patton was actually the one who'd disobeyed orders and rolled in, so the Russians weren't as popular here.

The helicopter was still stammering about and appeared to be dropping leaflets. My mother came out and we went to the park, to see what was happening.

Our glorious allies had moved in with their big toys, and looked like they were going to stay awhile, and none of us had any say in the business.

A bit later, we moved on to the main square, to the attraction of the day. This was an angry ocean of shouts and screams, people surging and banging fists on a couple of stranded tanks. Some tactical genius had decreed the Cathedral was a hotbed of capitalist insurgents, and the cannons of the tanks were pointed that way.

The crowd grew ugly, pounding on the hatches and turrets. Someone had even climbed up and stuffed toilet paper in the cannons themselves … and the soldiers cowered inside, not daring to show their faces.

I saw the old photographs again recently; the shouting faces and clenched fists, and the one officer sticking out of the turret, his arms in a helpless shrug.

He is holding out a crumpled map, almost as if beseeching the crowd to help him find his way.

The soldiers had been lied to, told they were on tactical maneuvers in Hungary.

—We are all of us lost, and the strings get pulled every which way.

I Can't Forget
Townsend Walker

TWO WEEKS BACK IN MUNICH and I think I've found the peace I'd come for. Munich is, as I remembered, a felicitous town with musicians on every corner: Mozart concertos, Bach sonatas, a Billie Holiday tune here and there. Even the heavyset gothic Cathedral of Our Lady is lightened by choirs singing hosannas to the Highest. It has been four years, no breaks, since Will was killed and I joined up: Officer Candidate School, Special Forces, language school, deployment. More about that later.

On Wednesday I strolled into the gardens leading to the Städtische Galerie. The museum is housed in a gold-colored Tuscan villa, once the home of the painter Franz von Lenbach. The first gallery was filled with people smiling at Klee's colorful and cheerful work: Southern Gardens: vivid orange, red, blue and green-blue patches. And Rose Garden: carnelian, cerise and scarlet geometric figures.

The next gallery was strangely deserted. Klee's Ravaged Place hung on the far wall: a bruise-purple building with dabbled white roof is askew in the background of the painting. It once had four walls, but now, almost like a stage set, only the building's façade remains. Its gaping window holes are shaded violet black, wraiths curling behind them. Two smaller structures tilt in from outside the frame. Their windows, too, are vacant eyes to the sky. In the foreground, are headstones and two forgotten mines.

My mind flashed to the scene we'd passed on the last patrol. It had been a long day. We'd beaten off two insurgent attacks and were within a couple miles of base. Over the ridge we saw the village. Smoke still curling. Crumbled dun colored mud houses. Wooden framing sticking out at unnatural angles. A parched flattened land. Fragments of clothing fluttering from splintered windows. Blackened shards. Blood streaked arms and legs, and a doll, littering the ground.

I slumped, found a museum bench, sat down, my head in my hands. My heart was pounding. I was nauseous, like the time I was in the back of an old bus and traveling down some broken-up mountain road breathing diesel fumes and greasy mutton. I kept tasting the sausage I had for lunch. It was hot and I couldn't get up, trapped between two men, asleep. I squeezed my head tighter and tighter to quiet the clattering explosions going off in my skull.

Dad, a Nam vet, never told me about this. But he was career; maybe it's different for them. My twin brother Will had followed Dad's lead. He didn't have the chance to tell me; he died at Shahi Khot in 2002. I'd stayed away from everything Army, until what happened to Will. He was so enthusiastic about helping the Afghan people; I had to finish what he started. That's the way it was with us, we'd done that for one another from the time we were two.

* * * * *

Someone struck me. I jumped; nearly knocking the man down. Slowly, I saw him, the attendant, a thin wispy-haired man carved by age. I was back in the museum.

"*Bitte*, are you well?" he asked.

I'm sure he'd only tapped me on the shoulder.

"I'll be fine, *danke*."

"Me, I never come in this room," he said. "Too many thoughts, too many memories I don't want to have."

Looking down at him, I asked, "Der *zweite Weltkrieg*?"

He nodded and mumbled, "Stalingrad. I can't forget."

He looked at me, eyes filling with tears. His lips moved, but no words came out. Finally, he placed a thin arthritic hand on my arm, and held tightly; comradeship across wars and years.

I walked slowly out of the Galerie, and back through the Plaza of Our Lady, hoping the music would salve the memories.

That evening I was taking the train up to Frankfurt for my flight. Leave was over. I'd be at my command in Kabul in twenty-four hours. In a way I'm glad. I'm not haunted by memories there.

Kashmir 1987
Alamgir Hashmi

This is the blue-stone river
on whose banks the fairies danced at midnight.

The Neelam burbles through the city
echoing the language of undulate margins
which these valleys understand.
Its sound rationalizes even the mountains

and the pointed spires of land
reflect in its flowing photography.
The division of water is not
an issue here as down south,

for the Bald Mountain, discreetly snow-capped,
watches over the city and the country
holding right the balance of the deeds,
the annual cut of land against the water.

This is the blue-stone river
on whose banks the fairies danced at midnight.

The Neelam goes through the city
humming an old tune
that time can crack as fresh walnut,
while the valley's fruit collects

in wicker baskets and the cease-fire holds.
These houses are wingless words on the page,
but glow-worms
        f l i t t i n g   i n   t h e   b r e e z e.

Is Not Every Moment Kurukshettra?

Robert Hampton

the golden age ended and the iron age
began on the Plain of Kurukshettra,
when human chronicles were pilgrimage
meditations sung like Kurukshettra,
where still sing heroes of Kurukshettra,
and how long it lasted, the golden age
when no noble blood soaked Kurukshettra,
has long been the query of saint and sage,
yes, has long been the quest of saint and sage.

is it so difficult to see how lead
can be turned into gold? entropical
energetic behavior, the cold, bold
second law of thermodynamical
conclusions regarding the musical
spheres, displays, as it does, a dispersal
of cause through effects time demands equal,
like the eventual, emerging circle,
Kurukshettra, the modern miracle.

thought, sound, form, and like a flame being born
there is increase, thought, sound, form and decrease.
the ancient ones knew that knowledge of torn
standards at Kurukshettra would increase
understanding of how all wars may cease.
so while it may appear there are countless
wars, there really is only one, and peace,
like a sun shining in the shadow less
absolute, is one's state of consciousness.

The True Development of the Atomic Bomb
Kyle Hemmings

As THE STORY LEAKED OUT, Fermi refused interviews.

Then, Oppenheimer admitted before a small press conference that the Manhattan Project owed its success largely to the efforts of a secret player on the team, a mute with savant-like abilities, a man he referred to as Weinberger. Actually, I had given him that name.

Some say that as a child Weinberger could learn piano keys easily as hopscotch. And I could testify to that.

At first, General Groves refused to comment on Oppenheimer's statement. Later, he confirmed it. A Los Alamos reporter dug up information that Weinberger went mute after being traumatized by a childhood rape. Several women came forth, claiming to be Weinberger's biological mother. One such woman called herself "Baby Doll." But I had taken Weinberger under my wing during the Depression, adopted him so to speak, as we hitchhiked along the East Coast, standing in soup lines, so, I dismissed the women's claims as irrelevant. As I have always speculated, Weinberger was either an escaped orphan or a runaway from an institution. Whenever I said the word "mother," he would stare at me queerly.

Some say that after the atom bomb was dropped, Weinberger's voice started to come back. They said his attempts at words were inarticulate as a foghorn, that he often lisped and stuttered, skidded over his sibilants. I, for one, have never heard Weinberger speak except with his hands and sad, blue eyes. On several occasions, I witnessed Weinberger as a child, throw temper tantrums, beating himself on the head or kicking old rattan chairs, when I could not understand him. After traveling with Weinberger for some ten years, living off the kindness of strangers, staving off the cold and rain in the warmth of their houses, we became separated after a flood hit lower Georgia. I had given up Weinberger for dead.

After the war, while I was recuperating in an army hospital after having my leg amputated, I received a letter written in an unfamiliar script, saying that I was invited to a ceremonies award in Washington, honoring Weinberger for his contribution to the outcome of the war. The letter was signed—Betty W.

The room swarmed with reporters and important-looking military staff; men often shook hands with each other. There was a grand piano towards one corner of the room. I squinted to find Weinberger. He smiled warmly and waved at me. My heart jumped. Why it was years since we were together, fleeing from the muddy waters, getting lost among Georgia Knolls, marshlands.

Oppenheimer delivered the opening speech, claiming no amount of scientific background could equal the breakthrough in fission that Weinberger had discovered. Everybody in the room cheered. One man, obviously a veteran, remarked how many land mines still remained in Burma, and another shouted out that the cheap production of ball bearings could have a positive effect on the post-war economy.

Mrs. W., in a black sequined gown and beehive hairstyle, approached the podium. Exuding the eloquent pose of an Eleanor Roosevelt, she stated that since her husband would not speak before large groups of people, he would play an etude on the piano. Weinberger, barely five foot five and intensely shy, made his way over to the piano, and began playing Chopin's 4/4 tempo to perfection. Then, as if possessed by some demonic force, he started hammering the black keys, causing an uncanny sensation of thunder striking the room. Over and over, he kept banging those black keys. I watched as many women in the room gawked, or held their hands over their ears.

Mrs. W. walked over, slammed the piano case on Weinberger's fingers, causing him to wince, to cry a shrill howl. Some of the women in the room covered their mouths with cupped hands; I watched several generals cringe. Then, leading Weinberger by the arm, she strutted out of the room. We listened to the clicking of her heels, echoing down the hallway, until they faded, like memories of our own mothers.

But now, none of that really matters. None of that matters at all. What matters is that I imagine Weinberger is making slow, but nevertheless, significant strides in speech, perhaps curling himself into a ball when he fails, like the times I chided him for not being able to speak as a child. And he will play Chopin's etudes under the supervision of his wife, until he gets it right.

Mahatma's Change
Shanna Karella

"We must be the change we wish to see in the world."
—M.K. Gandhi

Remember the day the wars all stopped?
When soldiers discarded cause
and rushed to assist the
wounded; lifted them all up
and bore them from the glare
of conflict into peace?

The day poverty ended, by popular
assent. When the people moved
en masse to stand between injustice
and social class, freely sharing,
Remember how green it was? That the world
was changed as we stewarded resources
and rebuilt ecosystems, preserving
and nurturing the very ground that cradled us.
The sky cleared, leaving our eyes to water
for other, kinder reasons, and we smiled.

Beliefs were shared, which led from discourse
to understanding and respect. We built
on accord, considered intent over matter
and saw the truths enfleshed in all
like rare coins in a palm. Remember?

Chapter Two
The Sacred Arunachala

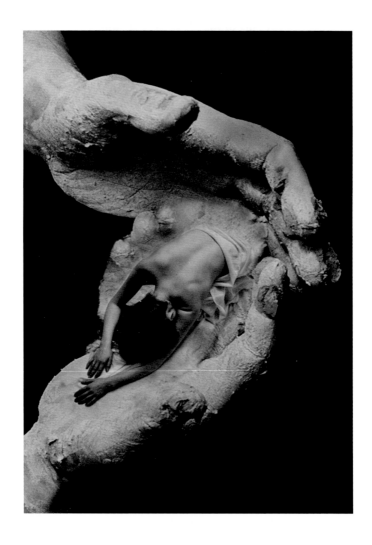

Dolphins Smile
Kyle Hemmings

After my brother OD'd on his wife's
fair-weathered love,
I drove to the coast
in his old convertible,
welcoming the stars in the front seat,
and a moon that only smiled
out of a celestial courtesy,
I dug my feet into sand, into earth
that could swallow me whole
keep me dumb in its vast womb,
I wandered by the coves
and dreamt of sailboats
in a squall of sky
and which one my brother would captain.
I watched the dolphin-girl,
been spying on her for weeks,
walking along the tide's edge and sweep,
tossing seashells back into an ocean
of forever lost and found again,
the neighbors said she went crazy and mute
after she lost her husband and baby,
how she'd stare when spoken to
and just smile,
just smile like a dolphin,
like some sonar secret
she won't give away.
Tonight, I won't give in
to the gravitational pull
of the earth's darkest core,
I trudge up to the dolphin-girl,
startled, she stumbles back towards the waves,
then slowly, she works her way to me.
I think of how the moon will fall

will float on the sea,
and Newton must recalculate
the motion of solitary apples
as I bear witness
to this galaxy of strange frequencies
between us,
there is only us,
the last of the damaged dolphin-people
as we stand facing each other

I smile
she smiles.

Green Shade
James S. Oppenheim

A green shade the wind moves
On currents of ash and smoke
White as cancer, dry as bone
My evening hour is spent
Meditating, inhaling
Birds sing mysterious codes
Branches sway their dark leaves
Moths gather at the porch lamp

Senryu
Jeff Haas

Are we doomed or damned
To witness our extinction?
Doomed or damned, which one?

Nigerian Health
Mike Woof

WHEN NSE, ONE OF THE TEACHERS I was working with, showed me the badly infected wound on his thumb, I winced at the sight and said, "That looks really painful."

He explained how he'd cut himself while working on the patch of land where he grew some crops and how he'd tried, unsuccessfully, to clean the wound afterwards. Because of the rural environment and a humid climate that bred microbes, injuries like this were commonplace in Uruk Ata II. I'd seen several like it before. The infection had penetrated deeply into his hand as the tip of his thumb now oozed sickly, cream-colored pus.

"Yes, I have to go to the doctor in Abak and get a penicillin injection," he said. "But it is costly so I will have to wait until our salary is paid."

"Are you sure that's what you need?" I asked, mindful of the fact that if this wasn't treated quickly it could require the removal of the entire thumb. For Nse, who used his farm plot to supplement his income from teaching, this would be a major disability.

"What do you mean?" he responded. Nse was direct and to the point.

"Well I think I can wash out the wound," I said. "And I have an antiseptic powder that'll help with the infection. It'll save you having to make the trip to Abak and paying for the injection."

"You think this will work?"

"I think so," I said. Although the infection had penetrated into the thumb, I was confident that I knew how to clean it out. It was common sense surely. "At least I can stop it from getting any worse," I added.

"When can you do this?" he asked.

"I'll come over after school," I said, "But there are a few things I'll need," I added and explained what I'd require.

When I got there, Nse's wife had boiled a pot of water, left it to cool and poured in some disinfectant as I'd asked. "Put your hand in the water," I told him and warned, "It is going to hurt."

Nse dunked his hand in the warm water, made milky by the disinfectant, which still swirled in streaks slowly around the bowl.

"Can you pour some disinfectant over my fingers?" I said to his wife, so she unscrewed the cap and did as she was asked. She was a strong, practical woman who was assistant head of the local primary school. They were well matched. Nse was my height but had the stocky build and muscle of a rugby player. He taught English and religious education and was scrupulously trustworthy. While he could be infuriatingly self-righteous at times I'd never blame anyone for a trait I share. Moreover I liked both Nse and his wife. They'd been very friendly when I first arrived in the village, stunned at the enormity of my move, and I owed them a favor.

I knew the warm water would soften the skin in his hand and make it swell a little. It was common sense. Ever so gently, I squeezed the pus out of the wound, only stopping when a streak of red blood joined the creamy swirl of disinfectant and pus in the bowl. This had to hurt as it meant the disinfectant was now inside the wound. But Nse was as tough as nails and didn't make a sound. His only reaction was to tense his arm.

I lifted Nse's hand from the water and inspected my work. No more blood had appeared. Next, I picked up the antiseptic powder and said, "This will probably hurt some more," and sprinkled it on.

Again, Nse said nothing.

I picked up the piece of cloth that was soaking in another bowl containing boiled water with a dash of disinfectant and began to tie this tightly around the wound. "I'll take the bandage off tomorrow and have another look at it then. I may have to wash out the wound the same way again if it doesn't start to heal," I warned and Nse nodded.

"If I have to wash it again, I'll need to have the boiled water with disinfectant in," I said to Nse's wife and she nodded. "If you want to change the cloth around it that's okay, but make sure the new one is clean and it'd be a good idea to soak it in boiled water with disinfectant just like this one," I added. "Okay, see you tomorrow at school," I said.

Nse nodded. "Thank you, you are a good Christian," he said and patted me on my shoulder with his good hand.

When I unwrapped the bandage the next day it was clear the wound had begun to heal. It wouldn't need to be washed in disinfectant again, for which I was probably more pleased than Nse. It was amazing how quickly the wound had scabbed over and I could see the angry red swelling had also gone from his thumb. "It won't be long before you can use your right hand again to do that," I joked. The problem with living in a village is that news spreads quickly, as I soon found out.

A week or so later I was riding my Honda to the river where I wanted to have a swim and wash my clothes when someone waved at me from the side of the bush track. He was in his early twenties and looked familiar, "I am Idiong and you teach my sister," he said and then I recognized him. He regularly brought his sister to school on their father's motorbike.

"What's up?" I asked.

"One of my father's workers has an illness. He wants to know if there is a pill that can cure him."

"I don't know what I can do. I'm not a doctor."

"Can you advise him? It would be very helpful. I heard what you did for Mr. Nse. He is an elder in my church and speaks very highly of you."

Somewhat warily I said, "Okay, I'll see if I can help but just remember, I'm not a doctor and if that's what he needs I'll say so."

Idiong led me into his father's compound. A small, wizened man stood there. He looked ancient, though he was probably only in his forties and in all likelihood had been aged and shrunken by a tough life of hard work, deprivation and semi-starvation. Idiong repeated, "He wants to know if there is a pill that can cure him."

The man looked at Idiong, who nodded. They'd clearly discussed this earlier.

Then the man dropped his trousers. I was shocked at what I saw but I didn't have to examine the patient to see what was wrong. His swollen scrotum hung past his knees.

"Er, I don't think there's a pill that can help," I said. "It looks like a hernia or some kind of rupture to me. He needs an operation. Does it hurt when he lifts anything heavy?"

Idiong translated this to the man who nodded slowly in response to my question as he raised his ragged trousers. I don't know who was more embarrassed, the man or myself.

However Idiong seemed oblivious to this discomfort. "Is there anything he can do?"

"Well if he lifts anything heavy it might make it worse," I said, knowing this advice was useless. The man was poor and obviously couldn't afford the operation he needed, so the problem would most likely get worse and worse until he became unable to work. With luck he'd have one or more children who'd be able to provide for him, otherwise he and his family would starve.

"I'm sorry," I said, feeling useless and ashamed at what I'd seen.

Idiong walked me back to the Honda and said, "Thank you," and then I kick-started the bike and rode off along the twisting bush track to the river.

Ghazal
Shanna Karella

Away with the guile in the pace of your eyes!
Don't measure and weigh with the trace of your eyes.

I feel each whip on my skin of your lashes,
soft brush me again with the lace of your eyes.

No more can I take accusations from you;
I burn with the fanciful race of your eyes.

Our love a ghazal, we've sung out in a crowd,
their response turns to trust the brace of your eyes!

Where's kindness, compassion or peace in you now?
What monster is this in the place of your eyes?

As lovers caress, we take comfort within.
I wish for just this: it's the grace of your eyes.

Like two fists, your will ever batters me down;
no one can withstand the brute mace of your eyes.

Aging has claimed your thoughts, words and volition.
I see only dark in the space of your eyes.

Each day is a joy, Cy, a touch or a smile:
No more than the simple embrace of your eyes.

A Time Long Ago . . .
Bill Frank Robinson

In a charity ward
an old man lay dying
swept from the sidewalks,
garbage, destined for
an unmarked grave.

Eyes closed, lips moving
words unknown to
those listening,
a Mexican girl arrives
to interpret.

The words flow, non-stop.
The girl giggles, hand clasped
tightly to mouth,
giggles out of control,
head moving side to side.

She reaches out, pinches the
great toe, his eyes
pop open, "Cabrona!"
He growls, but with a
hint, just a hint of a smile.

The impish girl giggles,
mouth clasped tightly,
head shaking, "No!"
The old man dies
with a smile.

Chapter Three
Say Unto this Mountain

Sunset
Ajay Prasannan

Life in Calcutta
Cleveland W. Gibson

CALCUTTA POVERTY SPREAD ITSELF across the flux of city life. In this city, where I was born, my grandfather showed me the faces of beggars without food or water, slumped in doorways, men down on their luck, no homes or family, many with diseased eyes. Few treated them with compassion.

My grandfather encouraged my sister and me to take an interest in those unfortunate beggars. We gave away our pocket money, and even adopted one. Food left over from the table, clothing, anything that might help, was given freely. Our beggar's smile was the only reward we needed. This experience brought home a message about poverty and humanity, though at the time we were too young to know precisely what it was we were learning.

When the British Empire folded, we returned home. In England, the contrast to our circumstances was beyond belief. Yes, we had water and some food. But, we were refugees from the world I knew, refugees of circumstance. Now, our family was stricken by poverty and it hurt. We accepted food parcels from the local church at Christmas time. Somehow we managed to keep a positive outlook.

Significant poverty still remains in Calcutta. I often cast my mind back to those we'd never got around to helping, millions of them. If only . . . if only things had been different.

New America
Nick Bakshi

SHE SQUEEZES MY HAND, pulling me to a stop. "This is what I've been waiting to show you," she says. She points a finger, draws a line across the horizon. My eyes follow helplessly.

It's New York City in red and gold—steel and concrete against a burning sky. She's explained it to me many times, but it's not until now that I understand. I scrape my shoe against the pavement, pick the grit from my nails, imagine what it would be like to live that far off the ground. I think to say, "It's beautiful," but only manage, "You were right." She pauses, then replies, "New Jersey is no New York."

We stand together, staring out—watch the sun climb the sky and crown the city in white and gold. "That's the New America," she says; my heart quakes at the miles between us.

We'll part soon—I to work, she to her mother's house. She'll dress and feed her sister's children there, hum melodies from a place long forgotten. My melody has been drowned out, lost in the hum of a thousand tireless machines. Her coal black eyes plead with me now, We'll come back here, though. Won't we? And I promise that we will.

Our walk winds down a set of broken stone steps, past a sign that reads, High View Park. The letters are crooked and faded, the wood yellowed and rotten. In my mind I see a man; leathered hands, wrinkled smile, paint-streaked clothes and sun-baked skin. A half-choked breath warms my cheek; I'm tugged along again.

The path drops through the trees, into the parking lot below. A dumpster in the corner overflows with trash. The wind grabs an empty can, whips it across the jagged pavement, grinds the edges to a sheen.

We reach the car. There's not a thought between us now. The rusted doors are wrenching back; we're off before we've fastened in, before we even know which way to go.

The Death of Apollo in the Kansas City Bus Depot Men's Room

Robert Hampton

a homemade noose and a place to hang out
a rhythmic dance in stinging fumes of bleach
gaseous chemicals and stopped-up toilets
in the eternal doorway a worn sole
macabre pirouette on the wet tile floor
stained trousers creased like road maps opening
and closing containing miles in themselves
dangling an inch above their reflection
weightless weightless at last weightless at last

Limbo
Shanna Karella

Perhaps we linger here, bereft
of beauty—tantalizing this
first glimpse of green buds, a breath

of soft wind on bare skin, cerulean
sky rolling slowly into night an aching
distance out of reach—and pause

for one last look, our former future
now irrevocably past. This juncture,
with its promise and pain, both

momentary and infinite, where we
regain perspective, is a blessing.
Our hope, that tiny glint, beckons

through this bleak and airless
night in which we float. Far off
is light enough by which to see

that still our children play,
unconcerned at the change
in gravity; unaware of the risk

that living is, or that transformed
we each, alone, must make this leap
into the unknown and undeclared.

Huron Cemetery
Robert Hampton

the insects in the breathing grass hiss high
notes like piccolos in a gathering band
or wind rushing through the mask of the one
who makes medicine. arithmetic
is axiomatic where so many
surrendered now to the absolute lie
in collective memory or selective
interpretation of what constitutes
valor, dignity, immortality.
how many heroes? how many cowards?
how many divine souls in average roles
arranged here now like sentinels within
the waning spin of a dying town's walls?
how many renovated listening stones
in fading white with european names
mark aborigine bones like *george i
curtis,* chief of the wyandot nation?
how many shamans struck a warrior's peace
like helena floating voice conley?
how many were strong as a living rock
in gardens of the gods like swan peacock?
apologies to grave grey poets aside
there are no sentimental feelings here
like lust addicts lurking about the grounds.
death, rather, is like a breath for warriors
and for those somehow involved with warrior
lives, and their silent watching is signaled
by light pervading the air like a mist
among stones, three o'clock in the morning
and by hidden songs in the thriving grass
praying for the barbarian hordes to pass.

Huron Cemetery Revisited
Robert Hampton

hear the desperate, whispering alleys,
hear the crack toreadors abandoned
in haunted corridors; hear the plaints
of poverty shuffling through empty streets;
hear the wail of the wino baying prayers;
observe the people huddled on dark stairs
and reflect upon the nature of death
on this sacred hill in winter's cold breath.

perhaps some day when the town is played out
when the buildings are gone and the heartland
can be seen alive in the wind, someone
to whom the great spirit returned
this land, knowing the signs of a hallowed
place, will perceive the grand reclamation
while gathering pieces of stone with broken
names and singing sacred words to sacred flames

Walking on Red Brick Road
A. *Jefferson Brown*

WE LIVED OFF RED BRICK ROAD, a little path of a street that the county never saw fit to pave. Our house sat in the woods, with oaks, elms, pines and cedars. Wild animals roamed about our eight acres, but Daddy didn't seem to mind—he said they were part of nature and nature was just fine with him. It was fine with me, as well.

The old log house we lived in wasn't too big or too small. Since it was just the two of us, I always thought it was just right. If Momma would have been around when we moved in—I was about four at that time—then maybe we would have needed a bigger place. But as it stood, Momma was dead, killed in the city by some drunk driver with no conscience at all, and it was just Daddy and I.

Daddy was a strong man with big arms, broad shoulders and rough, calloused hands. A lot of folks were intimidated by his size as well as this look he got on his face when he was angry. I only saw that look once in my day, when I skipped out of school in the eighth grade to go to Bessie Mae Hallerin's house. Bessie Mae's daddy wasn't too happy about it, and neither was mine. When he picked me up at her house he looked madder than a pit bull with rabies.

"Get in," he said and thumbed to his truck. As I went, I could hear Daddy talking with Mr. Hallerin. It grew heated. By the time I reached the truck, Daddy had growled something about, "It takes two to make a baby." Kids were kids back then, and in the eighth grade, making babies never occurred to me. Sure, I wanted to kiss her and all, but I didn't know much about sex, except what I heard at school, and I didn't rightly believe any of them stories. Daddy didn't say a word as we drove. I glanced over at him a few times and he was chewing—not tobacco or gum or a toothpick. No, Daddy chewed on nothing when he was mad. It was like he was grinding his teeth together, trying to keep his mouth shut so he wouldn't get any madder.

I just knew I was in for it when he got me home.

"Go to your room, Jesse," he said as he sat down at the table.

I had learned you don't argue with him. I went straight to my room and lay on my bed, nervous as all get out, waiting for Daddy to come in and lay his leather strap to my backside. A couple of hours later he knocked on my door and entered my room.

"Dinner's ready. Go eat, do your chores and get to bed."

That was it. No beating; no yelling; no nothing.

"Daddy," I said in the middle of dinner, "aren't you gonna whoop me or something?"

"You're too old to be gettin' whoopins, Jesse," he said and put a spoon full of stew in his mouth.

"But, aren't you mad?"

"Jesse, I'm disappointed. You know better than to skip school. You need to get your education and you ain't gonna get it messin' around with Bessy Mae."

"We didn't do anything. Honest, we didn't."

"I didn't say you did—I'm just disappointed. You know better, and I'm going to tell you this: if it happens again, I'm gonna lay a beatin' on you right in front of the little lady you're skippin' school for."

We sat in silence for a long while. My dad stewed in his anger, which I could handle well enough, but him being disappointed bothered me more than anything. He took great pride in me, and I had let him down. It played on my mind as I finished my dinner and cleaned the dishes and the bathroom. Just before going to bed, I went out onto the porch where my dad sat, smoking a pipe and looking off into the woods.

"Daddy, I'm sorry." It was all I could muster.

"I know you are, son," Daddy said and stood. He stepped over and gave me a hug and did something he hadn't done since I was little. Daddy kissed me on the top of my head.

"Get off to bed—you've gotta lot of work to do tomorrow."

As I went inside, Daddy called back to me.

"Jesse, that Bessie Mae sure is a pretty girl."

That was my Dad—he never let the sun set on his anger. I made for certain to never get that look again, to never disappoint him that way again. Daddy was all about lessons, but he was also good about making sure I knew about the world and my surroundings. And he was always there for me when I needed him. He talked about life and love and Momma, whom I barely remembered.

"Come on, boy, let's go for a walk," he'd say and I knew the walks meant we would talk. The mundane stuff came first: How's school? You playin' sports this year? Still have your eyes on Bessie Mae? That kind of stuff. Then, he would point things out to me; the trees, the ground, the sky, the animals. As we stepped onto the old dirt drive that led to Red Brick Road, he would talk about how things were when he was a kid and how I had it tougher than he did, especially since Momma was gone. He would say 'your Momma' like she was still around or something, as if he didn't want to mention her name for fear of me maybe asking more questions than he had answers for. Like, why was Momma dead?

When we reached the end of the path, Daddy looked out at the world, at the beautiful land around us and smiled. Sometimes there were tears in his eyes and I pretended I didn't notice them, just like he pretended they weren't there.

Old Red Brick Road became a path of lessons for me and, after a while, I longed to take that walk. Reaching the end of it was always the highlight, even during some of the sadder talks where Daddy mentioned how things were when Momma was around.

My first day of school, we took that walk and Daddy told me it would be okay and that I would get through the day, even though I was terrified. I didn't much believe him, but he'd been right. When I went off to college, Daddy walked me down that dirt road. He looked at me and smiled. Again, he told me it would be okay. I was welcome home anytime. I got a little adventurous in college, but I always made my way home. When I graduated, instead of staying in the city, I went back to our little town; back to the log cabin in the woods; back to Daddy and those long walks we shared.

"Let's go for a walk, Daddy," I said to him one day after coming home from work.

"Everything okay, Jesse?" he asked.

"Yeah, Dad. I just want to go for a walk."

For the most part, that was the truth. I wanted to walk with my Dad but I wanted to tell him something important; something I thought would change my life forever.

Like all the other times, we talked about the everyday stuff we could have discussed over dinner. When we reached the end of the driveway, the sun was setting and Daddy turned to me.

"So, what's this all about, Jesse?"

"I asked Bessie Mae to marry me."

"Well, what did she say?"

"She said *yes*."

Daddy clapped me on the back and gave me a hug. "Congratulations, Jesse. I'm proud of you, Son."

"Thanks, Dad. I want you to be the best man."

Daddy looked at me with his aging eyes. Tears began to fill them, but none of them dropped. "I'd be honored to be your best man, Son." The day I got married Daddy walked with me again. He told me things about my Mom I never knew, including how she died and why he moved us away from the city. All them years of him fighting back the water works finally gave way, tracing from brown eyes down the side of his face. Daddy took off his wedding band. Then, he reached into his bib-alls, pulling out Momma's wedding band too.

"Here, I want you to have the rings, you and Bessie," he said and placed them in my hand. It was the greatest day of my life, stunned and honored all the same. I had both the people I loved most with me— Bessie Mae and Daddy. Bessie wore Momma's band and I wore Daddy's. I could have never been happier.

On my thirty-eighth birthday I took Bessie and James, my son, to see my dad. James was still too young to know him as much more than 'the old guy that gave him treats.' I knew something was wrong before I got out of the car.

"Dad," I said and ran up the steps to where he sat in his old rocker on the porch. His pipe lay on the floor next to him and he didn't seem to notice me. I shook him and said, "Dad, what's wrong?"

When he looked up, it hit me. He was no longer the man of steel he was to me when I was young. "Daddy" had become "Dad." Age and life had caught up with him. His hair was grey and his eyes faded brown. He blinked several times and it appeared he was back from whatever wonderland he had been in when I drove up.

"Jesse?" he asked, his voice full of confusion. "What are you doing here?"

"I brought the family by. Remember, I called you last night and told you we were coming."

"That's right," he said and tried to stand.

"Dad, you don't have to get up," I said.

"Son, let's go for a walk."

"What?" I asked. I was dumbfounded. My dad looked like he was dying and he wanted to go for a walk.

"Let's go for a walk."

"Dad, I don't know if that's such a good idea—I think I need to get you to a hospital."

"You'll do nothing of the sort," he said, his voice suddenly strong. "I want to go for a walk. Is that too much to ask?"

"No, Sir," I said and reluctantly helped him to his feet and down the steps. I motioned for Bessie Mae to go on in the house; we'd be there in a bit.

We walked our normal path, chit-chatting as we always did, though a lot slower than before. When we reached the driveway, Daddy looked at me. Reaching a hand out, he took one of mine and we walked the length of the driveway, stopping at Red Brick Road.

"Daddy—"

"No, son," he interrupted. "I don't have much time left and I don't want my grandson seeing me like this."

"Like what, Dad?"

"Dying."

I couldn't believe I had heard the word. "Dad, don't say that."

"It's okay, boy," he said, fighting back tears once again. "Don't be afraid. It'll be all right."

"But, Dad, you can't die—not now. Not ever."

Tears were dripping from my eyes as I begged him to stop talking such foolishness. But, it was true—Daddy didn't have much time left. I had known that when I drove up and saw him sagging in his rocker, his old pipe on the floor, that distant look in his eyes.

"Jesse, I love you, son," he said and put his arms out to hug me.

"I love you too, Daddy," I said and embraced my father. I held him tightly, even after his tears had dried up and his body began to sag. I felt one last breath on my neck and Daddy was gone. I laid him on the ground and sat beside him, cradling his head as I cried. I heard Bessie Mae's voice somewhere in the background and then a while later the emergency folk were there to take him away.

Long after the police and everyone else left, I remained sitting on the ground at the end of the driveway. The sun began to set. I thought how beautiful it was. Daddy was with Momma now. I hoped and prayed he was happy.

Every week I come back here, back to the cabin where I was raised. When I do, I sit in Daddy's rocker, holding his pipe in my hand, wishing he were here. Before I leave, I take a walk down Red Brick Road to watch the sunset.

Today's a little different, though. You see, yesterday we buried my Bessie Mae. After forty-eight years of marriage, she passed on before me, just as my Momma passed on before my Daddy. I now know what Daddy went through all of those years without her.

James will be here soon to take me home with him. I don't much want to leave, but he's concerned about his old man and wants to be there for me if something happened. I can't say I blame him; I've been in his shoes. Before he gets here, though, I think I'm going to take a walk and have a talk with Daddy. If I'm lucky, I'll get to see the sun set one last time from Red Brick Road.

Her Secret Wardrobe

Kyle Hemmings

She awoke
from a cornucopia
of stretched faces
a river of white noise.
In the oblong room
the sun hit her face
at acute uphill angles.
There was still the buzz
of a tenant's voice
in the next room.
At the window
she could see
anonymous birds
landing on hard pavement
snatching breadcrumbs.
She opened her closet
deciding which stranger
she would become today,
which thoughts to avoid
like starched collars
or a man's jeans
too tight in the hips.
There was enough
for this month's rent
and a dollar
for the subway sax player
who went blind
but never invisible.

Chapter Four
Decisions by Shura

A State of Becoming
Sita Bhaskar

"AM I "PRO-CHOICE" OR "PRO-LIFE," LOKESH?" Girija lowered nine-month-old Kanti onto the changing table and reached for a diaper. She spoke in Tamil, her native language, except for the words "pro-choice" and "pro-life" for which she did not know the Tamil equivalent. Lokesh leaned over the changing table and brushed his fingers lightly across Kanti's cheek.

"I don't know. We've never had that discussion before, have we?" he asked.

"We?" Girija held Kanti's tiny feet together and raised her bottom, sliding the diaper under her. "Why would we discuss that?"

"Then why ask the question now? You didn't have any doubts before Kanti was born." He paused. "Or did you?"

Girija opened the dresser and considered her choices. Lilac floral leggings or pink overalls? "Kanti? What does Kanti have to do with it?"

It was close to Kanti's mealtime but Lokesh stopped her from devouring the squeaky toy bunny for lunch by rescuing it from her pudgy fingers. Conversation not revolving around Kanti, conversation in full adult sentences between Girija and Lokesh had to wait offstage like actors in the wings waiting for a cue. Lokesh went into the kitchen to prepare Kanti's meal, while Girija dressed her in lilac floral leggings, quite forgetting that her question remained unanswered. It had been this way since Girija had started taking ESL classes. "English as a Second Language" took Girija on several forays into the cultural labyrinth. More often she felt like a camel—storing up chunks of spoken English to digest and regurgitate at leisure.

When Kanti was an infant, Girija had joined the "B4-One Mothers' Group." She felt like she belonged in it because the mothers spoke about the same things; the universal language of breast-feeding, teething, the color and consistency of baby poop. If she had been in Trichy, her hometown in South India, she would've discussed the same topics in Tamil. But when the B4-One-ers used words like "pro-choice" and pro-life" she worried about her understanding of the English language. What would happen when the B4-One-ers became After-one-ers? She would have to step up the pace of her ESL lessons to go beyond B4-One vocabulary.

"So, you guys became pregnant right after you got married and decided to have little Kanti here," a B4-One mother had asked at Girija's first meeting.

Girija nodded. There had never been any doubt in her mind that she wanted to be a mother as much as she wanted to be a wife. Not any wife, but Lokesh's wife. It was possible to fill two roles at the same time. Just like her father had been both mother and father to her after her mother's death.

"Must be a pro-lifer, huh?" said another B4-One mother.

Girija nodded again. She had no idea what the term meant, but with her limited English vocabulary she knew "pro" was good; "pro" was positive. The conversation lingered around this topic in the desultory manner that only mothers of recently fed and successfully burped infants can achieve, but Girija wasn't sure of the details. They could have been talking about breath fresheners or bubble gum for all she understood. So she busied herself with baby talk with the B4-One babies. As soon as the group dispersed, she stopped on the sidewalk on her way home and wrote the words "pro-life" and "pro-choice" in Tamil script in her spiral notebook. Lokesh would help her with their meanings.

The incomplete conversation with Lokesh, like punctuations in the sentences of daily life, was left unfinished, but Girija knew she could seek explanations in her next ESL class. The ESL classes had been Lokesh's idea. Left to her, Girija would have waited to learn English until Kanti went to school, becoming fluent grade level by grade level until Kanti reached high school and both mother and daughter would spout heavily accented American English at rapid-fire speed. But Lokesh had nudged her into ESL classes. "You have to engage in the language. Only then can you take part in everything that is happening in the country," he said. It sounded ominous to Girija, as if by learning to speak English she could suddenly find herself deployed to Iraq fully engaging in America's war for democracy—or was it on democracy? She hadn't engaged in the language long enough to know the difference; she would have to ask Lokesh.

Language. After all what was language except a means to communicate? Girija spoke Tamil. Falling in love with Tamil—a language—and pursuing a college degree in it was encouraged by Girija's father, a Tamil Scholar himself. If Girija's mother had been alive she would have steered her daughter to more practical aspects of life—an education in English as the foundation, with doors and windows opening to Hindi and Tamil, and the ebb and flow of the creative air of music and the arts. But Girija's father, immersed in ancient Tamil literature, had not been able to look ahead to the modern day world when Girija would have to leave his heart and home and pursue her own life. Falling in love with Lokesh was greeted only with the observation that he would carry her off to a non-Tamil speaking country.

It had taken Lokesh three visits from the cold climes of Wisconsin to the hot tropical weather of Trichy to lure Girija into accepting his proposal. If only the exchange of engagement rings and wedding garlands had been as easy as the exchange of suitcases that had led to their meeting. In a world filled with identical, expandable, upright, wheeled suitcases, Girija and Lokesh were the only two passengers on the train from Madras to Trichy who had not tied multicolored ribbons, bands, or bows to their unlocked suitcases as identification. So, it was not surprising that she pointed to the wrong suitcase amidst the clamor of porters and the booming train arrival and departure announcements on loudspeakers at the chaotic platform of Trichy railway station. The porter had picked up the suitcase Girija pointed to, heaved it onto his head and hurried down the milling platform with a petite Girija weaving in and out of waves of red-shirted, red-turbaned porters, passengers, luggage, and vendors in an effort to catch up.

Girija was first introduced to Lokesh through a faint whiff of cologne that floated out of his suitcase under the horrified gaze of her sister-in-law; her brother Babu's wife. And then with hesitant prodding, as if the owner of the suitcase had folded himself in with khakis, jeans and t-shirts, they pried an American passport from a large leather travel document wallet. And gazed at Lokesh Muralidhar, whose clean-shaven face with rimless glasses looked out at them with an earnest look that said, "Please find me soon and return my passport. I have to return to America." But how could Girija find a person even with the help of a permanent address in America when the person had arrived in Trichy by Rockfort Express? There was no airline manifesto they could check; this was the railway. The trusting nature of the American passport-holder was soon revealed by the complete absence of any identifying information in or on the suitcase. Girija pictured his life in America—unlocked doors, trusting neighbors, waking up to the glorious aroma of freshly baked bread that a neighbor had left on the kitchen counter, tiptoeing across a lush green lawn glistening with morning dew.

So they waited for the address pinned to the inside of Girija's suitcase to bring Lokesh Muralidhar to their doorstep. Which it did. And he visited them. Again and again. It was as if having met her suitcase he did not want to release it to the care of such a careless though enchanting owner and was determined to take Girija with him if that was the only way he could ensure the safety of her suitcase. His passport photo was deceptive; there was no determined chin, no set jaw, only a mildly serious look. The determined suitor was missing in the photo.

"I told you to educate her in English, Appa," Girija's oldest brother said, when Lokesh had returned to America with only his suitcase and no Girija in tow. "Now look at her. She had hoped to lose her heart to another Tamil scholar in Trichy, but she sent it to America in Lokesh's suitcase."

"English? What is language except words following a set of pre-defined rules?" Girija's father said. "Girija has the ability to weave words together, be they Tamil or English."

She did, in frequent phone calls with Lokesh, in hours spent with him during his next visit. "If he spends any more time in this house, I'll have to put his name on the ration card and get him voting rights in the next election," her father said.

Instead, Girija put his name on her marriage certificate and migrated with Lokesh to Madison, Wisconsin, with her degree in Tamil and a willingness to learn English. "Why use such obtuse words like *pro-life* and *pro-choice?*" she asked Lokesh more than a week after she first raised the question. She had engaged in several discussions on the subject with her ESL classmates in varying animated Chinese, Hispanic, and Middle-Eastern accents. "Why not say *against abortion* and *for abortion*? Everyone knows what abortion means."

Lokesh held Kanti at his shoulder and patted her gently on her back until she gave a loud burp. She reared her head up in surprise. Girija was *pro-life* in the general sense of the term. She was for life; she was all for the joy of living. Of course she was. She, who had lost her mother in grade school, knew the value of life. But was there no other way of saying it in America without standing on a political or moral pulpit?

"I believe in women making their own choices, too, Lokesh," she said, "deciding if they want an abortion or not. Is that morally wrong?" She peeped at Kanti over Lokesh's shoulder. Kanti squealed in excitement and held out her arms. But Girija had a special ESL session that evening, so Lokesh turned her around and walked her to the car.

The last ESL class was a special session for immigrant students preparing for their citizenship interview. The students quizzed each other in turns. It was strange to hear the names of all the presidents of America recited in different accents—Hispanic, Oriental, Asian and even European. The *Bill of Rights* was recited in lilting sincerity by Chinese students. The American system of government and the three branches of government was parroted by students from the Middle East. The Hispanic students sang the *Star Spangled Banner* while Girija, along with two men from Sri Lanka and a woman from Pakistan, recited the *Pledge of Allegiance*. The ESL teacher, an immigrant herself from Laos, capped the evening with a cake decorated with red, white, and blue icing in the pattern of an American flag.

Traveling outside the cocoon of her ESL class and the B4-One Mothers' Group to the immigration office in Milwaukee was a long mental journey for Girija. Having gained entry so easily into the sisterhood of marriage and the privileged world of motherhood, Girija worried about her final passage into the *Land of the Free and the Home of the Brave*. But the ESL classes held her in good stead and her application for naturalization was approved. Within a week she got a letter for her swearing-in ceremony. With careful baby steps she had entered her adopted country.

Girija held out her fingers and Kanti grasped them to pull herself up. "Look Lokesh, look," she said. Kanti took a few more new steps and flopped down on the carpet. Lokesh held out his fingers, looking towards the television. Kanti reached for his fingers but they were higher than she could reach. She toppled over with a cry, but Lokesh continued to look at the television. Then he turned it off with a snap and flung the remote on the sofa. Girija looked from him to the blank TV screen to the remote on the sofa. "I'm sick of these political campaign ads," he said.

"Oh, when is the election?" Girija asked. If they distressed Lokesh so much, Girija was relieved she could not understand rapid-fire television English as yet.

"Next Tuesday."

"But that's the day of my citizenship ceremony," Girija said.

"Will the ceremony get cancelled?" Girija was surprised to find that *Election Day* was not a holiday in America.

"You can vote right after the ceremony, Mrs. New-American-Citizen," Lokesh said.

"But I don't know anything," Girija said.

Lokesh held out his fingers to Kanti, still higher than she could reach. She swayed and bounced on her diapered rump until she grasped his fingers. "You are a fast learner," he said. Girija reached for the remote and switched on the television. Lokesh stretched on the carpet and indulged in baby babble with Kanti, while Girija listened to political babble on the television. Suddenly he sniffed. "What's that smell?" Then he held his nose close to Kanti's diaper and said, "Hey, Miss Kanti-poo, time for a change."

"That's what they are saying on TV, too," Girija said.

The next morning, a disheveled Girija carried Kanti into the breakfast nook. "It's just as bad as that *pro-life* and *pro-choice* thing," she said. She sat Kanti down on her high-chair. "Now I've got to sort out this *left-wing* and *right-wing* business. Even with only two major political parties, these campaign advertisements are so confusing."

Lokesh brought a bowl with a baby-sized serving of Cheerios and offered it to Kanti. He picked up one and held it to Kanti's mouth. She turned her head away. "Sick of it already?" he asked.

"Can you imagine the chaos if they had as many political parties as we have in India? But I'm not going to give up. I have one week to learn to do my civic duty," Girija said. Kanti took the Cheerio from Lokesh's hand and guided it into her mouth. "Bravo," he said.

By late afternoon Girija felt like the candidates were campaigning in her head, their messages pinging inside her brain like atoms in a molecule. Of course Girija said "*Yes* to Marriage." It had brought her Lokesh and Kanti, hadn't it? But it wasn't for governments to define what constituted a family or what a marriage was. In Girija's mind, a home filled with love, that's what constituted a family. So why all this ambiguity in America? America with her *Bill of Rights* and *Amendments* numbered sequentially from one to twenty-seven in whole numbers. How did India define marriage and family? She had to ask Lokesh. Her college degree had only opened her world to the rich literary heritage of Tamil. She had to learn these things for Kanti's sake, unless of course Kanti decided to become a Tamil scholar in which case Girija was adequately qualified. She switched off the television and turned to local news channels on the radio.

When Kanti woke up from her afternoon nap, Girija clutched her tight until the toddler squirmed and wriggled out of her arms. "Don't go too far," she said when Kanti toddled to the family room, as if outside forces were waiting with bated breath to topple her world. Lokesh arrived in time to see her switch off the radio. He held Girija and Kanti in the circle of his arms. "A right to vote carries with it the weight of things we can try to set right," he said. "But it is not a burden, it is a privilege."

Girija climbed the steps to the Federal courthouse in Madison with the constant din of campaign advertisements ricocheting off the walls of her head, crossing swords with the *Bill of Rights* and at war with the *Oath of Allegiance*. In the courtroom from where she sat she could see Kanti in her *Star Spangled Banner* dress perched on Lokesh's lap. Girija had parted with her green card and her Indian passport when she checked in for the ceremony. If disaster struck at this very moment, would only Lokesh and Kanti be rescued while she lay abandoned quite literally in no-man's land? How much power a government wielded with its laws of inclusion and exclusion. She felt quite alone. As the judge made his speech about the responsibilities of citizenship, Girija wondered about the burden of assumed citizenship. She had been born a citizen of India. It was just a state of being, not a state of becoming. Would she value her American citizenship more because it was an acquired status? Would the mantle of citizenship settle lighter on Kanti's shoulders because she was an American citizen by birth? Girija stood with the rest of her fellow citizens-to-be and raised her hand for the *Oath of Allegiance*—the quaver in her voice matched her trembling fingers. She released her breath only after she received her *Certificate of Naturalization.*

They were pulling into the driveway when Lokesh's beeper went off. Girija took Kanti into the house. "I have to go in to work, Girija," he said. "I'll take you to the polling booth when I get back. Is that okay?"

Girija waved him away. "It is time for Kanti's nap, anyway. After work will be perfect."

After lunch, Girija sat on the sofa and went through her citizenship goodies—a large white envelope from "The White House" with the words "A message from the President of the United States." Inside was a letter from the White House addressed to "Fellow American," welcoming her to the great and blessed Nation and signed "Sincerely, George W. Bush," a booklet from the U. S. Department of Justice, an antiqued copy of the *Declaration of Independence,* and a small American flag wrapped around a flimsy wooden stick. Girija spread them on the coffee table while the campaign advertisements played a crescendo in her head. She examined the flag to see if it was made in China as if that would sort out the confusion in her head, as if the election could be treated as a joke if it was. It was late afternoon when Lokesh called again. "Giri, there's a crisis at work. I won't be able to get away. Can you go to the polling place yourself?" Lokesh was a psychologist and was occasionally called in for emergencies, so Girija didn't mind going on her own. He promised he would get away from his office crisis long enough to cast his vote.

The campaign advertisements hounded Girija as she pushed Kanti in her stroller towards the polling place. The antiquity of Tamil, her own language with its rich literary heritage, had its aesthetics. The rhetoric spewed by current-day politicians in India were still understood by the common man because the same issues were spouted by all political parties dressed in different ways and showing different profiles to the voting public. How would India vote if a barrage of election advertisements worked as divisive forces? Sought to separate, to isolate by fear of exclusion? And keep a culture open to growth while shutting out certain groups on the inside? The perspiration on Girija's forehead chilled her skin on this cold November day. She dabbed at it with the sleeve of her fall jacket.

In the voting booth, Girija's brain on overdrive all day, screeched to a halt. All the campaign advertisements crowded in around her and jostled for space in the narrow voting booth, demanding her attention. They threatened, they preached, they shouted, they pleaded. "Vote *Yes* for *Marriage*," "Vote *No* for *Fair Wisconsin*." *Fair Wisconsin* had to be fair. How could she vote "No" for *Fair Wisconsin*? She thought back to her ESL classes and groped for the definition of "fair." Fair was free from favoritism, fair was being impartial, fair was without favoring one party. Everything in fair was positive. So *Fair Wisconsin* should be "Yes," not "No." Why did they say "Vote No for *Fair Wisconsin*?" Who said that? Was it the opposing group? She tried to elbow the campaign advertisements out of the voting booth, but they pushed back. She wanted her first vote to be "Yes." She would vote "Yes" to section 13 of article XIII of the constitution.

Marriage. Shall section 13 of article XIII of the Constitution be created to provide that only a marriage between one man and one woman shall be valid or recognized as a marriage in this State and that a legal status identical or substantially similar to that of marriage for unmarried individuals shall not be valid or recognized in this state.

Lokesh had not come home when Girija went to bed. It was past midnight when she heard the drone of the television downstairs and saw the eerie glow it threw on the pastel walls of the hallway. She stumbled into the darkened family room lit only by the glow of the television. "Lokesh?" she said. "What happened?"

He shook his head in disbelief at the television, as if he was accusing it of lying. "I can't fucking believe it. It passed; the marriage amendment passed."

Girija gave a very Kanti-like squeak. "It passed! I voted Yes for it."

Lokesh reached for the remote and switched off the television.

"Yes?" he said.

"Yes!"

He leaned over and switched on the table lamp as if he wanted to take a better look at Girija. "Imagine that. I had never taken a good look at you until this moment."

Girija snuggled up to him, picked up the American flag and waved it before his eyes. "Look all you want. I did it. I'm an American citizen. I voted." She hummed the *Star Spangled Banner*.

Lokesh took the flag from her and slapped it lightly against his palm with the thin wooden stick on which the flag was mounted. "You voted "Yes" for the marriage amendment?"

"I voted Yes for *Fair Wisconsin.*   Fair is yes, yes? 'Vote No for *Fair Wisconsin*' was the slogan of the opposing faction, no?"

Lokesh returned the flag to her, placing the stick in the palm of her hand and closing her fingers around it.

"No?" Girija's voice shook.

"It's okay, my heart. *Fair Wisconsin* didn't lose by one vote, so don't beat yourself up."

Girija flung the flag at the television. "I hate the English language. The *Bill of Rights* is a lie. All the *Twenty-Seven Amendments* are lies." She stood up and recited the *First Amendment* as if she were reciting couplets from the Tirukural, nonsectarian verses written in Tamil by Thiruvalluvar during the third century—in staccato beats of four words and three words. By the time she reached the *Third Amendment*, Lokesh rose from the sofa, put his arms around her and recited them with her. She repeated the beats until she reached the *Twenty-Seventh Amendment* and then started over again.

Breathing on Glass
L. McKenna Donovan

She knew she had to change the sheets, but as with any dreaded task, it was easier to do other things first. One distraction turned into two, which became three, and not until darkness made re-dusting the banister difficult, did Anne acknowledge she had done everything but.

She stopped short of their—no, her—bedroom. Not far enough, apparently, and she grimaced. Even though she had already crammed his clothes into garbage bags and dumped them on the front porch, his scent lingered.

Her sense of smell had always been good, but the second round of chemotherapy had made her strangely aware, sometimes to the point of nausea, sometimes to the point of acute regret. That was how she had known. When he had come home, the scent of sex on him was unmistakable, and her confrontation with him had been short. He had said 'you don't mean that;' she had repeated 'get out.'

"Mommy?" A small arm wrapped around her leg. "You gonna toss your cookies again?"

Anne blinked, then laughed and knelt beside her four-year-old daughter. "Now, wherever did you learn that phrase, hmm?"

"Mrs. Griffith. She said it was nicer than 'the green pukes.'"

The green, sharp nausea brought sweat to her forehead, but Anne concentrated on her daughter. "I think Mrs. Griffith is very wise, and I also think you need to scoot back to bed." Small arms begged to be picked up, then wrapped around Anne's neck as she indulged her daughter.

"Mrs. Griffith said it's gonna snow tonight. I love snow, just like you do."

Just like I do. Right. Anne kissed her daughter's forehead.

"Then you and I will go out and make snow angels. Now...back to bed with you."

"'Morrow'll be fun, Mommy."

"Yes, *'morrow will be real 'fun.'*" Anne tucked the covers over her daughter's thin shoulders and tapped her on the nose.

"Night, angel."

She eased the door mostly closed, pausing briefly when her daughter mumbled sleepily, "Wake me if you need a wash-cough, Mommy."

Anne smiled wryly, then yet again sidestepped the brand-new sheets that lay in the doorway to her room, this time to check the nursery. Well, not nursery, but "Edmund's room," as her son had solemnly corrected her on his third birthday.

As she expected, his blankets and pillows were crumpled into corners of the trundle bed. Anne had long since given up on keeping covers over the athletic sleeper, opting for heavy, one-piece pajamas to keep him warm through the night. He was asleep, thumb tucked into his mouth.

She returned to her room, scooping the sheets from the floor, and with them pressed against her body, stood at the window, staring at the black sky. *Please, dear God, no snow. At least not tonight. Not with tomorrow—*

She closed her eyes, seeing the long, slow miles to the city; seeing the nurses appearing, disappearing, reappearing, and the chemical cocktail dripping, dripping, dripping. And seeing the tedious hours back—she'd be alone tomorrow, no one to drive and no one to hold her when she began to retch. It was inevitable. She would have to stop for "the green pukes."

Oh, yes, 'morrow' will be real fun.

Lost in thought, Anne's hands dropped, and the sheets hit the floor with a thud. She looked down, startled. Oh, right. Sheets.

She stripped the goose-down comforter from the bed, then the thermal blanket and her pillow, but as she grabbed his, she checked her movement, then slowly clutched it to her body, inhaling the intimate scent of his warm, salty skin. Just that morning, he had said they should talk. Little did she know.

Anne lifted her head, exhaled sharply and tossed his pillow aside. "No more."

She tugged at the fitted sheet, but the deep pocket of the opposite corner stuck. Impossibly tired and impatient, she yanked, and it ripped as it came off, dumping her and the sheet on the floor. It didn't matter. She'd never use any of them again. She balled the linens together, then suddenly stuffed them into an old carry-on and dumped it on the porch with the other "garbage." She giggled. Let him smell her for a change.

The crisp, frigid air felt good deep in her lungs, but with her weakened immune system, it was dangerous to linger. Besides, even as tired as she was, she still had to get the sheets changed. Upstairs, she leaned her head and shoulders against the doorjamb and stared at the room. Simply changing the sheets would not be enough. Maybe if she moved the night stand to the other side. No, maybe the antique bureau with the beveled mirror. No.

The bed.

She had to move the bed. The voice that whispered "don't be silly" seemed to be his, and with grim delight, she wedged her hands, then one knee between the mattress and the box spring. With a heave, the mattress tilted up, but then collapsed against her, and his scent washed over her, exhaled by a mattress that had seen fifteen years of their marriage. Fifteen years of lovemaking and laughing and sleeping. And more recently, quarreling. 'If not today, then when," had been his question. 'Tomorrow' had been her response.

Fifteen years of marriage that could not be erased by simply tossing garbage bags out on the front porch. Well, she might never be able to scrub him out of her life, but she could certainly make it her life.

The bed.

She shoved and squirmed until the mattress finally shifted off the bed and thumped against the far wall. The box spring was easier, lighter and stiffer. The frame was easiest to move, and she defiantly shoved it in the one place he would never allow her to put it—right under the window overlooking the main street.

By the time the bed was reassembled and clean linens tucked into place, Anne's bones ached. Tomorrow, she would pay for her exertions, for sure, but today, she felt an unlikely joy, as if she had arrived, though where, she did not know. She turned off the lights, crawled under the new comforter onto her stomach and looked out the window. The windowsill was at the right level for her chin, and the glass was cold against the tip of her nose. The streetlight angled across the front yard, leaving all but a narrow cone of it in stark shadow.

The shifting of the bed covers brought a smile to her face, and Anne lifted the edge of the comforter to make room for her daughter, who squirmed up to the window and promptly set her chin on the sill next to Anne's and stared at the night.

"Whatcha doin', Mommy?"

"Breathing. Look." Anne huffed on the cold window, and a mouth-sized circle of moisture condensed on the glass. Both of them held still, watching as it slowly shrank, then finally disappeared. Renee huffed; again, they watched.

The covers shifted and dipped a second time, and a small boy's face joined theirs, chin on sill, nose against window. "'S'cold, Mommy."

"Look, Mommy! Edmund's breath!"

Anne tugged the comforter over her son and dropped a kiss on his strawberry blond curls. The children snuggled closer to Anne, huffing on glass, then watching and waiting. Something in the rapt gaze of her children, some hypnosis of the moment, made Anne focus on the glass, on each small blossom of breath.

Renee suddenly squealed. "The first snowflake!" The chubby finger cut through her last huff on the glass. "Quick! Make a wish!" On the other side of the glass, currents of flakes eddied closer, dancing through the illuminated branches of the old elm that stretched past the window. Flakes began falling faster, emerging from nothingness into the streetlight, spiraling as if on wings extended to the air, then disappearing at the whims of dark and light.

Renee and Edmund began betting. "That snowflake's gonna land in the light—"

"No, that one's gonna—"

"Mommy, that one's yours and it's gonna land on the window!"

Anne pulled her thoughts back from the dread of tomorrow, and let her gaze drift from the black-and-white scene below them to the animated faces beside her. Their exclamations and laughter condensed on the cold window, and Anne smiled, then leaned forward to add her breath next to theirs.

Continental Divide
L. McKenna Donovan

IT WOULD HAVE BEEN DIFFICULT to admit what I was feeling. Easier by far to focus on the hard, Wyoming clay under my heels, or on the bitter wind that beat against me and whipped my long, heavy coat against my calves, but the mourners deserved my attention.

"Beautiful service. So sorry for your loss." *Thank you.*

"So sorry. We'll be praying for you." *Thank you.*

"My dear, I'm glad you brought him back home to rest among us." *Thank you.*

"So sad. I know you'll miss him—"

—*Miss him.* My eyes turned to the burnished casket resting over the draped grave. Once the mourners were gone, the cemetery staff would come forward and lower the casket. After all, as the young priest had so solemnly promised from the graveside, "He was a cherished friend, son, and husband, and our memories of him shall remain untarnished and vivid."

Vivid. Yes, indeed, our memories of him—

A hand touched my shoulder. "My dear, will you be all right?"

I startled, then turned, thankful that a lash of wind brought tears to my eyes before I glanced up at the face above the black cassock. "Yes. Yes, I'll be fine, Father. Thank you." Despite my preoccupation, I realized how dismissive I sounded, and the good priest deserved better from me. I hastened to fill the silence. "Wonderful eulogy, Father, thank you. I know his mother will take comfort from your kind words."

"You're welcome, my dear." His hands offered warmth to mine, but his eyes? Yes, his eyes registered my slip—the inadvertent confession that the comfort of his eulogy belonged not to me, but to my late husband's mother.

"Julia-honey!" My grieving mother-in-law picked her way through clumps of brittle grass, stopping long enough to claim the priest's hands. "Oh, thank you, Father. Thank you so much! Yes, indeed, his last months were so terribly difficult...so hard on me, living so far away from him. At least he's home again. He was always such a fighter, but this? . . . Oh, he would have loved your sermon, just loved it. He had such a way with words. A lovely way with words..."

Yes, indeed, 'a lovely way with words.'

—No, no. The black dress. It manages to make you look elegant.

—No, no, no! That's not the way to do it. Here, I'll write your damned résumé.

—Just bring your proposal with you. No one at the barbecue will mind if you sit inside and work.

"Julia-honey?" His mother fussed her hair back under the stiff, black netting. "We're going back to the house. Everyone will be there, and Father Murphy is joining us. You really should—"

"Mum, his friends have come to see you, and I have to drive back home. I have only three more days of leave, remember? And it's a long way to—"

"—to Seattle, yes, yes, I know. Really, you should have flown so you don't have to drive yourself and I hate to think of you being on the road, particularly now that you're alone and things happen, you know—"

"Mum—"

"—and he certainly wouldn't have let you drive by yourself, especially at night and especially that far! Oh, dear, and it's so hard to accept that he is gone. My beloved son. Well, no help for that. At least he's home again. God giveth and God taketh away, you know. You'll come back for Christmas, of course. You're still family, no matter what anyone else says, and you'll feel better if—"

—if you wear the black dress...

—if you let me do it...

—if you come back for Christmas . . .

* * * * *

The drive home was suitably long. I refused to turn on the radio, the new silence too precious to fill with empty words—words of bright-speak disc jockeys, songs of love-sweetly-lost, promises of lifetime guarantees. Besides, the jagged mountains had always felt closer, more ancient and wise and intimate, without the sound of human voices. Maybe if I listened closely, the aspens would whisper their deep-rooted secrets to me—I immediately repressed the thought, but wait...there was no need. Old habits die hard, and it no longer mattered that he had never understood the mystic in me. I laughed, suddenly and joyfully, and it startled me. That was the first sound I had made in over five hundred miles. I rolled down my window and sucked the frigid air deep into my lungs.

With the window still open, I headed over the pass, but at the top, a roadside marker caught my attention. Another impulse, this time a bit easier to follow, I pulled over and stared at the sign. White letters on slate-blue background: Continental Divide. Around me the Douglas firs stood straight and tall and impressive, and the aspens shivered gold in the mountain wind, their leaves skittering across the first traces of snow.

Continental Divide. Behind me, all waters flow east, back to Wyoming, but in front of me, they flow west, onward to the Pacific Ocean. In my rearview mirror, I let the darkening sky hold my gaze for a long moment, but through my windshield, the sun was warm in the western sky. I set my mind toward the Pacific, the radio still silent, and my window still open.

The next day, the Cascade Mountains appeared in the distance, their winter shoulders sadly bare, for the year had been dry. Then several hours afterwards, I came over the pass, and spread below me was the skyline of Seattle and the familiar waters of the sound glinting under the late-evening moon. There was time to catch the late ferry, though I dreaded the crossing. As much as I loved to sit on the rocky beaches of the sound and stare at the million pricks of sunlight on choppy water, seasickness was my bane. This, however, had not prevented him from buying a thirty-foot cruiser. How long must I wait before selling it, I wondered, now that he was gone. The ferry was filled with passengers, some subdued from a long day in the city, but others, chattering, laughing, celebrating an evening's entertainment. Always the lovers arm in arm, and always the parents with children asleep against their shoulders. I did not get out of the car, suffering in solitude the pitch and shudder of the ferry caught by the strong cross currents of the changing tide. It did not help to count the minutes to dry land, so it was with great relief that I nudged my car up the ramp and onto dry land at the beckoning of the ferry worker.

An hour passed and the roads narrowed; four lanes became two, homes receded from the verge, trees laced overhead, and leaves slept in rain washed ditches. The house was deeply still, and as I kicked off my heels in the entry, I savored the silence. And the lack of his impatient voice.

—Did they sign the contract? Yes, but—

—Did you get your bonus check yet? Yes, maybe we could now—

—We should have children soon. You're not getting any younger, you know. Yes, I know.

* * * * *

It is my first morning alone. The house is open, windows and doors unlocked and unlatched and thrown wide to the morning air. The rough cedar deck overlooks the canal, and I watch the sun rise on gentle toes, traveling from the tips of the firs, down through the spread of branches before reaching their night-damp bark. My coffee is warm and darkly fresh, and I cup its warmth between my palms and lean my elbows on the railing. The tide is low, and the gulls forage for shrimp, crab, and mussels left in tidal pools by the retreating water.

The air smells green and damp, a bit acrid and yet vital. My collie-girl hustles to the shore, head lowered, her gaze intent on the flock before her. I sip my coffee and watch. She poses for a vivid black-and-white moment, then charges. The seagulls scatter and screech in a maelstrom of loose feathers and dropped shells.

I laugh, and the delighted sound carries westward over the water.

The Cat Skinner
Bill Frank Robinson

cat=caterpillar tractor or bulldozer
skinner=operator

All heads turn as he walks across the yard
Splendidly dressed, polished boots
Jodhpurs, crimson scarf
Leather jacket, leather helmet
Goggles pulled down to
Mask the face

Hard-bitten working stiffs whisper,
My god, dressed like an ace
From the Great War. All to skin the
Big Cat?

The Big Cat roars, bucks, shivers,
And shakes. The Great War ace
Grabs and holds, fighting hard
Against the force that
Threatens obliteration

The dust swirls, the new clothes
Soil. Fuel oil seeps
To the skin beneath
The soiled clothes

The battle rages
The Big Cat charging
The ace holding
The splendid clothes dissolving
Into a soggy mess

The day ends
The job complete
Time to go home
And face Mama

Mama screams, What did you do
To my boy? His clothes are
Ruined and he's only five

Daddy says, He's got to learn
To carry his weight
I started at four

Senryu: Truants

Elsie O'Day

ropes swing from tree limbs
sun and shadows dapple water
skinny-dipping boys

Cocinar Con Floralba
Shanna Karella

Alba refuses to let me help in the kitchen.
My Colombian sister-in-law clatters around,
chatters through the open window into the dining room
about yard work they've been doing.
I lean on the sill, sipping Yerba Buena tea
as she folds guava paste into creases
cut in plantains she'll bake for dessert.
My brother, six-foot-six of German stock,
walks in and swoops up his tiny wife.

"Ai, Mark!" She batters half-heartedly
at his construction worker arms; smiles,
embarrassed to have been caught
while I am watching. I grin, take advantage
of her diversion to sneak past them
and begin ladling Ajiaco into large bowls, on which
a thin patina of oil floats. As Mark puts her down
she recognizes my coup and throws her hands up
in resignation. "Is there anything else you want
me to do?" I ask, though I know she'll say no.

"No." Alba returns my smile as she dices
cilantro and tomato, knife rasping
against the scored wooden cutting board,
in preparation for the distinctly soupy
Colombian version of salsa she always serves.

Though I suspect she goes light on the peppers
for my sake, the salsa, like our burgeoning friendship
is spicy when swallowed, but not too hot.

Specimen #31, Adult Female
Ann Walters

Follow the fluid curve
of the iliac crest, sashay of bone
tilting into jutting hips.
Mirrored innominates flower
like twisted figure eights,
a triangle of sacrum wedged between
to form the ossified cup of the womb.

Run fingers over the narrow bridge
of the pubis, reading a Braille of birth
in pits and scars. The bones, still damp
from eight hundred years in earth,
hold a smell of thick life, reeking
rich decay.

Brush away the dirt with delicate tools
until only breath and a sliver of steel
can work the grains one by one
from the secret within—
an origami of eggshell bone,
the one unborn.

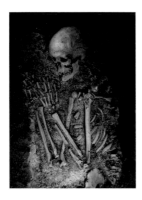

The Death of John Lennon
Kyle Hemmings

i.

On a day of dizzying sunbeams,
my feet light as a thin Napa wine,
a day so quiet, one could hear
the skin peel off yellow grapes,
I stood at the edge of the pool,
tucked my elbows, ready to dive.

There, at the bottom of the pool,
John Lennon's body, floating,
the cheeks bloated, the lips open,
ripples murky, shimmering.
I thought of kites lining the sky
watching them through clouds,
drifting, free from strings
that anchored them to tiny hands
tight as knots.
He was smiling. I could not be sure.

I turned to my new wife, Yoko,
playing cello on the patio,
and said, "Do you know John Lennon
is at the bottom of our pool?"
Her lips pinched as if this was
a mere inconvenience,
asked to pass a saltshaker
at the table, or yell at a
child rummaging in the attic.

"He's not dead," she said,
"he's merely free from the burden
of pretending to be a dead fish."
She resumed playing the cello.

For days, I walked, walked nowhere,
lifted on the notes, the vibrato of that cello,
walked through deserted streets and deserts,
not afraid of stray bullets, rabid dogs,
the iron fists of irate strangers.

Under the sole company of the sun,
I began to disrobe,
dropped this pretense of being something
for somebody else.
Or of having somewhere to go,
anywhere to go
when the whole world is a globe,
a grid of intersecting endings, beginnings.
And then, my flesh,
the sun-baked skin,
this thick barrier of coat,
this shroud of costly desires,
I would soon step out of that too.

ii.

The day after Lennon's death,
people huddled in Central Park,
drew Lennon's face on balloons,
released them, watched them float
over the trees and baseball fields,
over the high-rises and swank hotels,
while the crowd chanted the words
to *Imagine*. I could imagine.
For a moment, everyone became John,
the streetwalkers, the clerks,
the roller skaters, the carpenters.
When the song was over,
a hush fell over the park.

I had known Lennon all my life. In a sense.
Listened to him, my ear pressed against
a pocket transistor when I should have
been multiplying by nines, adding fractions.
Or later, hummed along to his words

in the front seat of my dad's T-Bird,
my hand snaking along the nape
of a girl whose face I can no longer see.

I left, nestled myself next to strangers
on a crowded subway, too immersed
in stock quotes and Iran's newest hostages.
My stop, the doors whooshed and screeched,
I climbed to the top of the stairwell,
spotted a woman slouched,
crying in a corner. Normally,
I'm not so disposed to approach strangers
who sell their small tragedies for hours,
as if their losses should be celebrity news,
and no one has anything better to do
than to sink time in a staggered line before a kiosk.

What's the matter, I asked. Sometimes,
a stranger can help you more than you think.
Her lips pressed. She turned away to the light.
I reached for a carrot from my briefcase.
Here, I said, eat a carrot. They're good for you.
I always bring a carrot to work but never eat them.
But they contain essential vitamins.
You really don't want to live without carrots.
You'd go blind. Or worse, you'd stumble at night.
Think of a world without carrots. And rabbits.
My God, what would the rabbits do? Or horses?
No, she said, she doesn't care for carrots,
the way your teeth crunch into them, the scrunch,
you can never eat them in a room of strangers.
Her lips trembled, she nodded her head at the carrot.
Said she just lost her job. Now, the rent.
Now, the kids. Now, nothing. And, God, her husband.
Why, the only thing she could afford now is carrots.
I smoothed her shoulder with slow circular strokes.
There are other jobs, I said, the city is full of them.
It's not something that's really taken away forever.
But, I said, this, here, there, what I once had, others too,
I'll never get it back. Do you know, I said.
What, she said, you mean the carrot?
No. No, not the carrot. You don't get it do you, I said,

What's all around us, colors fading, the echo of
subways through tunnels, the plaster across people's faces,
not even a sheen across tiles, nothing reflects back;
nothing. it's everywhere. Don't you see it?
What is? she said, what? If not about carrots. Tell me.
Please. . . Please. Please. Please. Please. Please.

Do you know John Lennon is dead?

iii.

Tonight, I walk the streets, me, a private world
among city blocks of such, as if our heads
were the kind of boxes children sometimes
cover their faces with, to block out the light, or
to sustain their new identities in a game of space aliens.
Tonight, the bars, their jukeboxes, play every song
ever recorded by Lennon, his son, Julian,
the duos with Yoko.
I remember how the crowd used to toss tomatoes
or how they posed nude to protest war, war of any kind.
And I wonder how it is that someone, so far,
far as dust or stars,
now, long ago, always,
never to revisit this planet
of untimely coincidences and new fads,
has guided me for so long
on this journey to now,
which is another name for never.

iv.

If I could take two steps back for each day of the week,
I'd wind up swinging the door out of Tower Records,
holding a plastic bag of new cassettes,
and then, stepping into the street,
the gun raising in slow motion, incremental steps,
I'd throw my body into the bullet's path,
an imploding burn, something final, more treacherous
then dying in a back draft,
my body crumbling to the curb,
and John, stunned, yelling for an ambulance,

Yoko pressing her hand against the hole
widening in the pit of my stomach.
This blood gushing, my silent, liquid lifeline,
turning to blue, turning to sky.
But too late, too late,
and I would never live to enjoy my celebrity,
this single act of heroism.
But at least, I'd figure, I've helped John
to make a hundred years
and at least ten more albums—or twenty.

v.

Slowly, they took John down from the cross.
Yoko Ono showed us the veil imprinted with John's blood
and sweat. Elvis showed up with the Colonel, he lay a heavy
Fender at the foot of the cross, said, "My brother, may we
meet again in rock n' roll heaven. The Liverpool Apostles:
Paul, George, and Ringo, crossed themselves, vowed never
to sign another record contract.

They cursed the Pharisees, the producers, the media,
the imitators, The A.M. stations, the censors, Cousin Brucie.
Yoko picked up a stone, inspected each and every
one of our faces. "Who sold him out?" she said.
"Who! It was all of us. Each and every one of us."
An old woman, perhaps from Syria, perhaps once,
a hip Hittite, hobbled over with a cane,
said her bed would be forever made of bricks.
Imagine sleeping on nails, or hot cinders, she said.
I carried John in my arms, his body, slumped,
growing lighter, the blood draining out.
Over there, said Yoko, heading the procession.

She pointed. "We will not bury him. Lay him there."
I lowered John on a hilltop overlooking the Sea of Galilee.
We bowed our heads and sang the words to Dear Prudence.
A young woman walked up to us, said she would never again
sleep with another man for money, food, this false tranquility
of flesh.

The crowd dispersed, a few argued over who should get
his platinum records.

"My husband," said Yoko, "his voice of wind and broken
pearls, may you rest in peace. The world will never
understand sacrifice.
Here. Lay him here. Where his flesh and bones will turn to
yeast, the bark of trees, the wings of a blackbird,
a filament of sky. In this way, John will become everything.
And everything is everything.
There will be no more wars of separation.
Everything is everything." Then, we treaded slowly into the
void of dusk.

vi.

Today I sit on the back patio
immersed in a swatch of blood-orange sunset.
Not even the buzz of my thoughts
could wake up the gladiolas, the insects.
Yesterday, my wife announced
that she was leaving,
without explanation or stretching the facts.
She left me with a jade of silence
& a whole cabinet of spice.
I should be thankful she didn't take
the old Beatles collection,
or the one with John and Yoko,
peaceful lovers under a tree,
the way we ourselves once designed
that summer of love.
We managed to survive a karma
of rainy days, a fondue of hopes
nettling the skin. We always wondered
just what happiness was.
& now with that buzz of thoughts
shifting to foreground, the drone of days
stretching out before me,
this empty goblet filled
with my distorted reflections,
Lennon and I are alone together again.

Dreams of Home
Sue Haigh

IT WAS MONTY DON'S ARTICLE in the *Observer* that made her want to take a train to London. Fascinated, she had read the words over and over again. With the aid of a magnifying glass she studied the full-colour reproduction of the painting, now on exhibition in the Tate Modern. This was Patrick's garden as she had known it when, newly widowed, she first moved into her Magdalen Yard apartment. That was forty years ago, half her life-time.

Nadia Bean lives on the second floor of a tenement on the edge of Magdalen Green, at number eighty-seven; a sandstone palace with towers and a halftiled close. High, curved windows look out over the Tay estuary and the sweep of the railway bridge and the long, empty beaches of Fife. At her gate, a brass plaque, worn with age and frequent polishing, informs passers-by that Nadia Bean, MSc, MBAP, FBPS, is a psychotherapist and that she sees patients by appointment only. It doesn't tell them that she first graduated more than fifty years ago and these days has only two regular clients.

Last week, Nadia had looked out from her kitchen window at the house and garden next door, quiet and lifeless since Patrick's death, the upstairs studio silent, his easel still in the window. The bareness of the plum trees and the straggling bushes and unmown grass and the length of the shadows and the lateness of the year made her think of Patrick and other things she hadn't thought about since she had watched her mother dying in a Toronto hospital. In the past few days she has twice thought she saw a woman walking slowly across the lawn in the late afternoon sun, hand-in-hand with a little girl, towards the stone wall that backs onto the mill-yard in Shepherd's Loan. The two figures moved with a proprietorial confidence which told Nadia that things in the garden over the wall were about to change for good. A sudden tightness in her chest, an unexpected sense of urgency, made her feel it would be too late if she didn't go soon. Just two days would be all the time she needed for a trip down to London and then she could see it again, the garden which spoke quietly to her of another world, before it went for ever.

It is Wednesday morning, a week later, and Nadia makes her way towards the railway station in a steady downpour, walking stick in hand, her shoulders hunched against the rain. Thunder-clouds have been hanging over Dundee since before first light and the smell of leaf mold and exhaust fumes hang in the late October air. Rows of gulls, clinging silently to the ridges of the high buildings, wait for the rain to stop so they can resume their raucous scavenging.

A treacherous slick of green lichen and damp leaves covers the pavements, dry since early in the month, forcing her to put out a hand to steady herself against the high wall at the sloping curve in the road, where Magdalen Yard becomes Roseangle. Rain is dripping steadily down the neck of her ancient brown waterproof, half-cape, half-coat with sleeves—chilling her spine, whilst the sandals she wears all year round squelch out water at every step. Up on the Perth Road, she sees the delicate glass-and-tile curve of the Frank Gehry arts center; it reminds her of a light-house teetering on a cliff-edge. The lights are already on, awaiting the installation of the next exhibition of the newest artists on the Scottish scene. Nadia loves exhibitions, especially paintings; but the great metal and rope concoctions that have pitched up at DCA recently, under its new young director, have left her dispirited. Mostly, they remind her of giant wooden gift-shop puzzles.

But, oh, when she thinks of Patrick—now Patrick was an artist you could understand; you could read his paintings as easily as you could read a book. And in his day the most publicity a young painter could expect would be at the annual diploma show, in the foyer of the art college in Bell Street. Nadia herself had sat for him when she was in her late thirties, or maybe her early forties. He had often admired her long dark hair and once remarked that her brown eyes and high cheek-bones gave her an 'air of detached exotic mystery.' During those quiet hours, whilst she stood at his studio window, gazing out at Magdalen Green and the river, he air-measured with his brush, stepping this way and that to catch a line, a shadow, watching her every expression with an intensity she had at first found unnerving. After two or three sessions she had started, hesitantly to begin with, to tell him her story—the only time she ever spoke of Nadia Oniga, the girl born into a Jewish community in Romania, close to that country's northern border; the only time she told anyone that, after the Ceaçescu years, nothing remained of those Jewish communities, nor of her birthplace, Iasi, nor of her family, nor of her history. Sometimes, she had rummaged in her pocket for a handkerchief, making him stop work for a moment. He had smiled and patted her hand silently, gently lifting her chin and adjusting an arm before he went on painting and listening, his habitual cigar clamped between his teeth.

Patrick called his portrait 'Nadia Dreams of Home.' When it was finished, he offered it to her for a good price, but, out of impecunious pride, she declined. For weeks, perhaps months, the painting was on show in the art dealer's window in Commercial Street. People would stop and examine the dark-haired woman who was staring at something far beyond the familiar Tayside landscape. Nadia walked past the shop window often. Then, one day, it was gone, bought by an unknown collector.

At nine fifty-five, the GNER Aberdeen to London train screeches into the station. A few commuters get off and Nadia hauls herself awkwardly into the first carriage. Her hips are aching from the effort of hurrying on the wet pavements and the struggle against the wind. She sits down and closes her eyes for a moment or two before taking off her soaking raincoat and folding it carefully on the seat beside her. The welcome heat of the carriage makes her head feel heavy after the chill rain. A young woman unwraps herself from several layers of coats and jackets and settles into the opposite corner. She switches on a small lap-top and Nadia opens her eyes at the trilling of Windows XP. She likes the technical noises young people make—sounds of life, promising the future. The girl reaches for a mobile phone and bleeps through a list before stuffing an ear-piece into her left ear and tapping furiously at her keyboard.

After a few minutes Nadia loses interest and her thoughts turn again to Patrick's garden. It was neat and well-kept when she first arrived in Magdalen Green. Sometimes, she would see him working out there. Not gardening—it was his wife who dug and planted and mowed—but painting. On sunny days, even in winter, she would bring out the washing, and hang out great white sheets to flap like the wings of gigantic birds. Patrick's small daughter would climb into her mother's laundry basket and clip the pegs round the edge, fencing herself in, whilst their dog scrabbled madly in the flower-beds laid out by the previous owner. The simple, universal act, the pegging out of sheets, watching them billow into the wind, straining at the line, as if they wanted to be somewhere else, took Nadia down distant roads in her memory.

The garden is different now, neglected. More natural, Patrick would have said. A bit like her own life, lately. There is no washing-line these days; the posts stand forlorn and unused at the corners of what was once a lawn, now chest high in wild flowers and grasses when spring arrives. No sheets to blow in the evening sunshine. The little girl grew up and left the garden long ago. Patrick's wife died, then Patrick. These days, the gravel paths are scarcely visible beneath a thick blanket of weeds. Only the plum-trees are unchanged; but no one harvests the August crop now; the purple fruits rot in the long grass, inhabited by swarms of wasps. The mill, across in Shepherd's Loan, is still there, now transformed into luxury apartments.

The gentle rocking movement of the train between York and Peterborough and the soft, regular tap-tapping of the computer keys lull Nadia into a half sleep. Her mother, Elisabeth, is singing a song in Romanian as she carries the washing out into her garden in Iasi. Nadia Oniga plays with her dog at her mother's feet. She can hear the flamenco-like rawness of Elisabeth's voice quite clearly; she feels the dampness of the sheets as they blow against her face. The train is hurrying the Onigas out of Iasi, their escape the start of a terrifying journey across Europe, often on foot. An image of her father floats into her dream. She sees Litzu Oniga, a graduate in ophthalmic surgery from the great universities of Cluj and Arad, selling spectacle frames on the street in a Toronto winter, barely surviving his new poverty in the New World.

By the time she was sixteen her parents' constant yearnings were an unbearable irritation to Nadia; the Carpathian Mountains, the forests of Transylvania, childhood holidays on the Black Sea, Mangalia and Constantia formed the backbone of their daily talk. She saw how they missed the dark sands of Mamaia and wished they wouldn't drone on about a past which, as far as their daughter was concerned, might as well not have happened. In her half-consciousness, Nadia sees again the longing in their eyes as they remember fishing trips with their own young parents on the Danube delta.

On the London train, Nadia feels again the inexpressible lightening of her soul, the wild bird beating her wings in her own sky, the same relief she had felt when her parents had finally accepted that they would never return to a country she could hardly remember and a language she could no longer speak. At the University of Montreal she met and fell in with—though not, as she later emphasized, in love with—and then married a Scottish Jungian psychoanalyst, Harry Bean. Harry's death at the age of forty-eight was a secret, guilty relief—a guilt she had confessed only to Patrick in the quietness of the hours they had spent together in his studio. She told him how, by the time they moved to Dundee, Harry had already been in the habit of taking a bottle of the 'Craythur' to his morning clinic, then in a white terraced town house at the smart end of Windsor Street. She wondered aloud how it was that his patients did not detect the slight, but constant, slurring of Harry's words and the redness of his eyes.

'My dear Nadia, they did notice. Believe me, they did.'

She misses Patrick. Now it's as if she is going to see him again.

By four o'clock the light is already fading. The young woman with the lap-top leans across and shakes Nadia's arm gently, nodding towards the platform as the train pulls into King's Cross.

Nadia is hungry, but there'll be time to eat later. She tells the taxi-driver to let her out at St. Paul's. A fine, soaking drizzle has begun to fall. A cold breeze makes her shiver as she walks slowly towards the river-bank and the Millennium Bridge—a swaying cat's cradle strung out across the Thames, so delicate it could take off like a giant winged insect, shaking its human parasites into the dark water below. Not a crossing to be undertaken lightly. Not a bridge for the despairing or the foolhardy. No parapets to lean over or to make a desperate leap from. The concrete tower of the Tate looms above the trembling filigree of silver birches on the South Bank.

The foyer is quiet as she looks down briefly into the Turbine Hall. People are lying on the floor, like tiny, distant ants, looking up into the mirror far above their heads, like part of the exhibit. She heads for the escalator. The signpost on the first floor tells her that the Art of the Garden Exhibition is due to finish today, at seven o'clock.

Suddenly, it's in front of her, just as it was; Patrick's garden, with his wife and the child and the dog and the sheets on the line and the shadows on the grass and the bare plum-trees, just as if they had all been waiting for her to arrive, to come home. She swallows hard, feeling in her pocket for a handkerchief; but, in the end, she doesn't cry.

This is what she has come to see. She thinks about Monty Don's *Observer* article. Didn't he know that this wasn't a morning scene? Had he assumed that no-one would hang out the washing in the evening? Didn't he know that the house faces south, across the estuary and that the shadows on the lawn come from the late afternoon sun? And did he know that the Victorian house which is casting the shadow was bought for a knock-down price in 1939, located in an area designated as unsafe in war-time? Patrick himself had told her that.

Nadia rummages in her handbag for her reading glasses and peers at the plaque beneath the painting. It reads: 'A City Garden' by James McIntosh Patrick, 1907-1998.

A young woman is leaning against the wall in a corner of the otherwise empty room. She walks across to Nadia and stands behind her.

"Do you like it?" she whispers, leaning into Nadia's ear. "It's Dundee. According to the catalogue, it's one of the most important urban landscapes on exhibition in Britain today."

Nadia turns her head towards the voice. She sees the woman. Dark hair flows down over slim shoulders; dark eyes, set above high cheekbones, dream of a distant world.

"I know." Nadia's lips shape the words silently. "I just wanted to see it again, before it's too late." The young woman nods and smiles, then steps back into the shadows.

Patrick, James McIntosh (1907-1998)
A City Garden, 1940
McManus Galleries and Museum, Dundee

Under Christian Crosses
Marie Lynam Fitzpatrick

OSIRIS WATCHES as his medley of souls twinkle through the arms of
Orion and the kiss of Artemis overhangs his realm. His sky lights the
Nile and his breath blows the feluccas as they drift on the current
that once carried Moses. Luxor awaits the first splash of dawn.

The back streets are empty but for packs of dogs and cats whose ribs
rise up through lack-luster coats. And, the horses, used to pull tour-
ists in traps during the day, are tied outside high row houses situated
on dirt streets. Here, old men smoke water pipes in the cool of the
night. They sit on doorsteps under Christian Crosses that are em-
bossed on the timber doors over the brass letter boxes.

The streak of gold, violet and reds switch the skyline and silhouette
the neon that straddles the McDonald's sign.

Osiris waits while Luxor dresses Thebes, Osiris watches patiently.

Remarkable

Dean Lawson

WHILE JOGGING THIS MORNING I saw a single leaf, autumn red its color, float its way back to the tree from which it came and attach itself to a branch. Leaving the park I saw a group of people at the gate, police were preventing anyone from entering. Asked if I had seen anything out of the ordinary. I lied and said I had not.

Upstate New York
Ralph Smith

Chapter Five
We Are As the Mountain

A Laotian Village
Kulvinder Singh Matharu

Hiking the High
(and lonesome)
Paiute Trail
Bill Robinson

Walking stick high
across my shoulder,
moving up off
the valley floor
into the cool, breezy
mountain air,
head down
climbing, climbing
reaching for
eternity
grab a boulder.

Look
ahead.
A figure moves
oh so slowly,
deliberately.
She comes,
face smothered
with wrinkles
lips flaccid,
hair like
the billowing
clouds.

A Paiute
woman,
stone-faced,
evil sparkle in her eyes,
silent words.
"What gives?

Flirtatious?
Mischievous?
Malicious?
What gives here?"

"Maun'-Naa'-Hoo!"
she shouts,
"You're older than me!"

Laughter meets
laughter
crashing, bouncing
off the canyon walls.

Salt

Oral Testimony, Neng Xiong

WHEN MY HMONG PEOPLE COME TO MINNESOTA from the refugee camp in Thailand, a friend says, "Neng, put a coat on. It's so very, very cold in Minnesota."

I think to myself, but never say out loud; *a coat. Sometimes I like a chilly wind. It will be okay.*

As I step off the plane in my cotton shirt, I am stinging from February winds. I am scared. And all that salt—everywhere.

I think to myself again; *who wants to live in a land of salt?*

I Love Life
Kyle Hemmings

La Première Fois.
Kyle Hemmings

I never figured into anyone's dreams
of heroes and villains
never had a rainbow tongue
a Swiftian wit
a body chiseled by Jake.
Always felt like a crossed-out item
on last week's shopping list
Until I met Sally Jasanewski
serving pastry at the bakery
on 14th and 3rd.
I held an incredibly rich
jelly donut between my fingers
and poked the middle
until the jelly dribbled
plopped and Rorschach-streaked
across a freshly-mopped floor.
I watched Sally's wide eyes
dance and her lips drool.
Right then, I knew
there was going to be something
between us
I could taste it like a flaky Ladylike
it was going to be something
cannoli consuming and deep-fry hot.

Touch of Wrinkled Skin
Sita Bhaskar

"THAT BUILDING THERE. No, not that one," Balaji said, as if her eyes were in his head, set below his eyebrows shaped like the wings of a bird in flight. "Yes, the other one, with each balcony poking a tongue out at the city." It seemed to Uma that every high-rise building in Bangalore was doing just that as she peered into the distance past her husband's pointing finger. "Did you find it?" Uma nodded. "Now, just three streets behind that is our house," Balaji said.

From across the city, it was hard for Uma to imagine their thirty-year-old house with polished red floors and shuttered green windows crouched amidst the new buildings of this concrete jungle. She wondered if the view was the same from her son's apartment just five floors below this one. Before he bought the apartment, had he stood at the balcony and looked past buildings stacked like Lego blocks back to a childhood spent playing cricket and *kabaddi* on quiet summer afternoons, redolent with the fragrance of jasmine flowers? Or past the late evenings filled with the heady scent of clusters of night-queen flowers, or *raat-ki-rani* as they called it? But—Uma reined in her imagination—her son had not hand-picked his apartment. She reminded herself that his investment advisor in America had selected it from a brochure. A glossy brochure that peeled away the sleepy pensioner's paradise and exposed a modern Bangalore donned with a fresh coat of technology innovations and fiber optics wizardry. Not for her son to agonize over the selection of foyer tiles, shade of wall colors, or veneer of teak wood doors. Not for him to worry about the space between adjacent ornate iron grillwork on the balcony lest an overactive child slip through and fall fifteen floors onto the terra-cotta tiles in the courtyard below. Only for him to watch the value of his assets snake upward in the hushed confines of his investment advisor's office. If it were not for this invitation to Swami's housewarming ceremony, she would've had no other excuse to journey past her hurt and come to the building where her son, Vishnu, owned an apartment.

"We should go in and circulate," Balaji said. Uma realized that he had been watching the expressions on her aging lined face. The smoke from the *havan*; the sacred fire inside, had sent them out to the terraced garden. Uma followed her husband through the French doors into the vast living room and sat down on a *dhurrie;* hand woven cotton rugs spread across the marble floor. She would've preferred to sit on the cool floor, pass her hand over the smooth surface, lean back against the freshly painted walls, and imagine that this was her son's apartment. Even through the haze of the smoke she could see the gleaming granite counter top in the kitchen. There was no shortage of building materials in these days from the global economy boom.

"How do they expect me to pay sixty *rupees* a bag for cement?" Balaji had said when they were building their own house in Bangalore those many years ago when cement manufacture was controlled by the government.

"That much? I thought it was sixteen *rupees*," Uma said. But supply at that price was controlled. On the one hand, the authorities approved building plans; on the other, they restricted the purchase of cement. Not everyone had access to corrupt officials who could waive the quotas. And somehow she could not see Balaji greasing the palms of these officials.

"Of course if we pay in foreign currency the government will release more quota for us," Balaji said.

"American dollars?" Uma asked, as if she had *francs* or *deutsche marks* stashed away and only American dollars posed a problem.

Balaji sat at his desk and did extensive calculations in his ruled notebook, as if he were solving a difficult mathematical equation.

"We could ask Vishnu, could we not?" Uma's tone was tentative. One could ask a son living in America for small items—things that did not skew the baggage allowance restriction on international flights. Where did bags of cement figure in this exchange?

For three days she watched Balaji disappear after lunch and return in time for his afternoon coffee that he drank while making even more complicated calculations in his notebook. On the fourth day, she saw him take out a thin blue aerogramme from his drawer. Even though it wasn't Sunday. Letters to Vishnu were written every Sunday after the morning meal. A letter on Thursday meant the matter must be urgent. Balaji took his fountain pen to the inkwell and filled blue ink in it. He sat down at his desk and covered the aerogramme with his neat, closely spaced handwriting, stopping to consult the numbers from his notebook. Then he left the house to mail the letter.

Uma was in the kitchen when Vishnu's reply arrived three weeks later. "See what your son has to say about my request," Balaji said, flinging the aerogramme on the kitchen counter. Her son—as if Balaji had nothing to do with Vishnu's birth. Nothing to do with raising him. Nothing to do with educating him. Nothing to do with sending him to America for higher studies. Uma switched off the stove and picked up Vishnu's letter. I have no interest in real estate in Bangalore, his letter began, and went on to chastise his father for trying to circumvent the national cement shortage and succumb to the government's greed for foreign currency. If sixty rupees is what it costs for a bag, I'm sure everyone else building a house at this time is buying it at that price. When Uma came to the sentence, *Cut your coat according to the cloth, as you've taught me since childhood*, she dropped the letter back on the kitchen counter, switched on the stove and continued with her cooking. Balaji had waited till the third loud clatter of a dropped vessel rang through the silent house. "Don't break all the vessels in the house. Maybe the government will start controlling the supply of stainless steel next."

"Did you tell him?" she said, the spatula making a ringing sound against the pan. "Did you tell him you would give the money to him in rupees?"

"What do you think?" he said. "That I asked him to get us the cement for free?" He switched on the radio and she returned to her cooking, feeling that she had uttered an obscenity by asking him if he had bartered correctly with his son.

Uma forced herself to concentrate on the religious chants sung by the priests as they welcomed the Gods and Goddesses of good health and prosperity into Swami's new house. When it was time to leave the house-warming party, Balaji took the wrapped gift from his bag and gave it to Uma. "With our blessings," she said, and handed the gift to Swami; the son of their dearest friends. Uma raised her hand as if to bless him, but instead ran her fingers over his thick black hair. He belonged to a chosen generation, as did her son where worry did not leave pathways of grey in otherwise black hair. Even if it did, Clairol and Revlon moved in with the efficiency of tar trucks and paved over the grey streaks with their hair-care products.

"Let us use the staircase and get some exercise," she told Balaji when they had said their farewells, slipped into their soft brown leather slippers, and collected Balaji's walking stick. Without a word he led her toward the staircase as if the trek down twenty floors was no different from their daily walk to the temple.

Even the stairwells were broad, airy and well lit. No shortage of cement there for sure.

During the days of cement quotas, in the months that followed Vishnu's letter, until their small house was built, Uma scrimped and saved as she watched Balaji *cut his coat according to the cloth.*

One floor was all they could afford to build. Nowadays it seemed that multi storied buildings sprouted and grew as fast as weeds. When they neared the fifteenth floor, Uma slowed down. "Do you want to rest?" Balaji asked, as if climbing down five flights of stairs was the only reason her breath quickened at the exact floor where her son owned an apartment.

"Why do you insist on clinging to that little house in Bangalore when you can come and live with me in comfort in America?" Vishnu had asked when they continued to struggle with the repairs to their house. But his interest in real estate had surged when Silicon Valley had discovered Bangalore and suddenly it became trendy to have had a childhood in Bangalore. As if a childhood in Bangalore had the same value as owning a home in a ski resort, or a cabin in the woods, or a cottage by the beach. Balaji opened the door from the stairwell into the broad well-lit corridor on the fifteenth floor. He led Uma to the window seat at the other end of the corridor knowing that it would take them past the door of the apartment that belonged to their son—an apartment that his investment advisor had him rent out to foreigners. Americans who wanted an apartment replete with the fittings of a western lifestyle, an apartment with a doorman to keep out the dregs of Bangalore of yester year. Balaji and Uma had caught snatches of comments in passing:

"Must be fetching a fancy rent, being rented out to foreigners."

"A bird's eye-view of the city from each window."

"And the city lights at night—a feast for the eyes."

As they walked past the apartment, they saw that the door was ajar, as if someone had known they were coming. Uma's footsteps slowed. Had the maid stepped downstairs to run an errand? But why use the main door when the apartment came equipped with a service entrance and separate elevator for hired help? They had just seen upstairs during a conducted tour of Swami's apartment, so she knew the layout of her son's apartment even though she had never stepped into it. What was life like in America to explain a door left casually open? If they walked into a holdup now, how would they explain their presence on the fifteenth floor when their invitation had been to a housewarming ceremony on the twentieth floor, in a building equipped with a doorman and an elevator operator, no less? These were the days of gated communities in Bangalore. Gone were the days when Vishnu and his friends would jump from roofs to compound-walls to branches of mango trees and back to roofs again to go from house to house. Gripping his walking stick, Balaji stepped in front of Uma, as if he knew what she wanted but did not want her to walk into any danger. They walked into the apartment.

A massive bouquet of long-stemmed red roses lay on a polished rosewood coffee table next to a cut-glass vase in the living room. With instinct honed through many years of tending her own rose garden Uma veered towards the flowers, picking up the vase to fill it with water. But Balaji stopped and looked back at her. She kept the vase back where it had been and followed him. Their feet sank into the luxurious hand woven carpet and muffled the sound of their footsteps as they followed the murmur of a female voice. They halted when they saw the curve of a shapely arm holding a receiver to her ear.

"But I'm so lonely and I miss home," the woman spoke into the receiver.

Inching closer to the doorway of what they knew to be a bedroom, they saw the gleam of a naked shoulder.

"Dan's always traveling and I'm miserable."

Balaji stepped behind Uma, more to protect the woman on the bed from the gaze of a male who was neither father, husband, nor son, Uma realized.

"Valentine's Day and I'm alone in an apartment in godforsaken Bangalore talking to my ex-boyfriend in New York."

The mass of shining hair on the spotless white pillow did not look mussed up. Uma wondered if the hair would lie flat against the woman's face if she turned around. Would her blue eyes—for it could only be blue with that hair color—open wide and look startled? Would she scream? Maybe she would recognize Uma as the mother of her landlord. Had she met her landlord, Uma's son?

"I'm afraid to leave my bedroom. Oh, I'll find two-dozen red roses in the living room, I'm sure. That's not romance, that's preprogrammed into his PDA and delivered on schedule as if I'm no more than a deadline to be met, a performance evaluation to be passed, and a bonus to be earned," the woman continued into the receiver.

Maybe the woman's husband had met her son in America. Maybe they were Vishnu's neighbors in the sub-division where he lived, walking across well manicured lawns and through geometrically trimmed hedges to join each other for backyard barbecues. Or maybe they had merely rented the apartment sight unseen.

"India was supposed to be about romance, visits to the Taj Mahal in moonlight, the gorgeous beaches in Goa."

The sun streamed in through the airy drapes covering the large French windows of the bedroom.

"Instead I'm stuck in this miserable apartment hung high over this mess of humanity." The woman sniffed.

With a bird's eye-view of the city from each window, the mess of humanity below was as busy as ants trying to eke out a living in a city they could no longer call their own, a city they had given over to the dictates of Silicon Valley.

"Oh honey, I want to come back to New York."

Uma and Balaji walked backward step by step as if in a choreographed dance until they reached the apartment door. They drew the door closed behind them and waited in silence by the elevator. "Ground floor," Balaji said to the elevator operator.

On the ground floor, they walked across the marble expanse of the lobby with well-tended indoor plants towering above them. Outside the building, Balaji reached out and held Uma's hand in his—not as if he were cautioning her to watch her footing over the wide polished stone steps. Not as if he were guiding her over a broken sidewalk but like a teenager, like a man fifty years younger than he, as if love could flow through the mere touch of wrinkled skin on skin and warm her heart. She tried to swing their hands between them as if they were young lovers out on a tryst, but at their age with her arthritic joints and his frail stooped shoulders they could only do one thing at a time. So they linked their fingers together and helped each other onto the sidewalk where they waited for a taxi to take them home.

My Grandmothers in Two Poems
Marko Fong

Her Will

i

Orange peel dries on accordion radiator,
goldfish in algaed shadows,
red cushion motel furniture
you, in your bed,
sewing, reading, chewing
Chinese newspapers, pumpkin seeds, mistuned television
No volume in your red orange world
across from the projects
yours alone for forty years.
"Speak up, she can't hear."
"Po Po" I shout,

ii

My "speak up" Grandmother
"School is not for girls."
Sin San pointed his teacher's finger past you.
You brought your own desk to that stone hut school
and refused to leave.
You kept a still during prohibition
behind the baby's crib.
You grabbed
brass-poled cable car
on the outside
the neighbor women, all shopping bags and
high pitched Cantonese shrieks
reluctant followers
to the bargain stores outside Chinatown.
You hand signaled the sales clerks,
grunted, shook your head for the best prices.

iii.

At the fish market, in a restaurant
you pretended not to notice
the woman with your forehead, your set of mouth
the grandson who held her hand.
She defied you into a thirty-eight year silence.
You left four million dollars to your three sons,
twenty dollars each to four of your daughters,
one dollar to the other.
You let your youngest son
hit your one dollar daughter.
"She doesn't matter,"
you told him.
Your eldest son
dropped his pants to the floor.
"Girls do the laundry for the boys."
"That's the way things are,"
you told your daughters.
You promised one daughter a six-inch circle of jade,
then slipped it on another's braceletted wrist.
"What promise?" you asked.
You watched her tears race against composure,
Your own face so many years ago in that stone hut schoolroom.
My 'can't hear' Grandmother.

The Ear

The most beautiful woman of your generation
they called you
at your husband's funeral,
intensity and clarity
that age could not wrinkle.
Men still stole dreams from your looks after your children had
children of their own,
ten pregnancies and six children,
one a miscarriage,
the other four, all visits to the midnight doctor
across town, the last time
you bled for six days, fainted in the bathtub
your everyday life
on a TV tray.
Solitaire with blue backed cards
game shows played in the background
while you counted money from the gambling house,
thousands and hundreds, clean and un-circulated
your hands
never stopped moving

But in your kitchen
hard rock Jell-O Chinese chewing gum, reindeer soup,
snails served on top of rice, corn puddle stew,
jook with marbles in it,
The only reminder of the poems
You wrote as a girl
In the deep scholar's Chinese
You taught yourself with help
from an indulgent father
"Inside blossom
 tear drop waits
 for night."

Sailing on, The Moon
Ivan Gabriel Rehorek

Sailing on, the moon is magic
headlights in the sky and starry traffic lights
and dancing the tire-black clouds go rolling on
servicing the carburetor days—

but just the same, sailing on, the moon
is magic chrome in the wind and sprays of leaves
streetlights marching like calendar days
the road winds on never-ending.
Pushing and shoving you've got to keep
the wheels rolling and the fare going
don't let the silence fool you
for the atoms themselves vibrate
with the music the symphony
of their own making . . .

And so the sun dusts its way to bed
and we again sit here watching
like we have for all our lives past—
laughing like the full rising moon!
Nobody ever got anywhere being
all left out and misunderstood,
so top up the tanks and fire the
stardrive *ad astra per ordur,*
whether it's pig latin or hen french
acts as fuel not fool:
and so sailing bounding it's all magic
nevertheless thinking of the beloved
and bemused smiling suns laughing moons
shining good-humored years
spilling the means of discontent
winters aside summers in mind—
and scrolloping, the clouds go whirling
past and past…

The Dream-Weaver's Son
Sue Haigh

Calcutta, February, 1947

Eenoo mclennan, en route from dundee to the McCormack Mill in Serampore, steps onto the gangplank of the *SS Narkunda* and gazes at the harbor far below. The acrid heat of the late afternoon sun hits him as if he has walked into a wall of fire and he wipes his brow with a rough handkerchief and stands like a schoolboy evacuee with his cardboard suitcase at his feet, waiting for events to overtake him. He looks up at the Howrah Bridge, hanging mirage-like over the River Hooghly, and across to the railway station. The roar and clamor of humanity make his head spin. On the quay beneath, vast crowds of people in family groups are lying on the ground, and cattle meander with leisurely confidence between the supine bodies. Dust has absorbed the humid rays of the sun until it is at boiling-point and blazing raindrops of light dance on the stones. Eenoo's shirt; one of the only two he possesses, clings to his back and beads of sweat run down his temples and neck. His ears buzz as if a swarm of the flies which ride on the backs of the cattle were heading straight for his brain via his ear-drums. Everywhere in the teeming, racketing streets, people who are not actually horizontal and sleeping seemed to be on the move as overflowing trams and buses rattle along, ploughing their way through the throng. There is a certain order in the mighty confusion of taxis, cycle-rickshaws, ancient cars, cattle and pedestrians as Eenoo bends down to pick up his case and make his way slowly down the gang-plank, carried along by the pushing and elbowing of the other descending passengers, now anxious to escape from their month-long incarceration at sea. He recognizes the platinum blonde woman who is mincing crabwise down in front of him, until she stumbles awkwardly over the boards, twisting her ankle as she tee-ters unsteadily on her three-inch red heels. Eenoo drops his case again and leans forward to break her fall. Recognizing her rescuer, Platinum Blonde sniffs mightily, glaring angrily past his left ear, then down at his feet and his shiny black shoes. She snatches her arm away from his hand as if it had been burned. With a disgruntled toss of the head and vermilion curl of the lip, she makes off down the steep gangway, leaving Eenoo to retrieve his belongings.

When he finally steps onto the teeming harbor, the familiarity of the faces of the Indian workers at home in the dark world of the Dundee mills fades into this sprawling culture, evaporating with the stench of stagnant spiced air into a smoky sky.

Seeing the mass of people crossing the Howrah Bridge, a longing to retreat to the fetal warmth of his tiny, airless cabin below the water-line of the *Narkunda* overcomes Eenoo. The explosive din and clatter of the railway station on the far side of the viscous river draw him like a magnet through the crowds towards the bridge. He has never seen so many people, even at the Overgate Carnival in Dundee. At the far end of the bridge a dilapidated sign announces the entrance to the Howrah railway station.

The McCormack Mill, according to the piece of paper in Eenoo's hand now, practically illegible after the number of times he has pulled it anxiously out of his pocket to study his employer's instructions as he paced the deck of the *Narkunda,* stands ten miles up the Hooghly on the riverbank. He studies the train-warrant, issued by McCormack's Dundee office.

"You need help, Sahib? Can I show you to your train?" An emaciated youth with a withered leg and rough crutches is squinting up into his face. He is even shorter than Eenoo. His open hand thrust forward. "Where are you going, Sahib? Is this your first visit to India? I welcome you and wish you much good fortune in my country."

Eenoo looks away, wary, not wanting to invite further intimacy from the beggar, but the boy stares directly into his eyes, smiling crookedly, one eye-lid drooping as if he has suffered a stroke, waiting patiently for an answer, his head on one side like an inquisitive blackbird. His hair, as black as Eenoo's, stands on end and his eyes, one of which turns inward, giving him a louche expression, are so dark that it is impossible to see where the pupils end and the irises begin. Eenoo cannot tell if the boy's lop-sided posture is the result of his deformity or merely an attitude of polite enquiry.

"Ah havnae a clue aboot the trains or yer rupees, lad," Eenoo answers, at last, embarrassed at his own ignorance in the face of the perfect English and courtesy of the almost naked youth.

"But this is not important, Sahib." The boy bows and gestures with the outstretched hand, placing it over his heart to show he is no longer a beggar but a new-found friend. "Tell me where you are going, Sahib, and I will show you to the right train. Where do you come from? Do you have a family? Why are they not with you here? Are they well? I hope I am not asking too many questions, Sahib. I will tell you about my family, if you like." The side-ways smile appears to have a life of its own as it fixes itself in place again. The questions, now that the matter of money is no longer an issue, trip off his tongue and tumble over one another like children in a sack-race, making Eenoo's head spin again. His only dealings with foreigners, apart from the mill-workers, have been with the Aberdonians who sometimes come down the coast to see their home team play United at Tannadice Park. And extracting a word from them is, as he likes to tell Jeannie, like trying to squeeze blood from a stone. When they do speak, their dialect is so alien that they might as well come from another planet. The young man persists. Eenoo can now see he is older than he appeared at first, his lack of height and physical substance giving an impression of pre-puberty.

"My name is Muhesh, Sahib, I was born here in Calcutta. My father's name was Chidam. He is dead, but my mother and sisters live near here. My mother is very unfortunate that she is blind and can only weave baskets to earn a few rupees and that her only son cannot work and has to sell her baskets or beg to keep her family alive. But she is a weaver of dreams. I would like to give you one of her dream-baskets, Sahib, to bring you luck. Tell me where you come from, please."

Eenoo hesitates briefly, but there is no hint of irony or self-pity in Muhesh's voice and his chirruping frankness makes a welcome change from the hoity-toity hauteur of his fellow-passengers on board the *Narkunda*, especially the platinum blonde with the vermillion sneer. Apart from the Welsh coal-master with legs like leeks, who would sing *Sospan Bach* at the top of his voice after two whiskies, and his wife with her floury raisin muffin of a face, none of them has, in the space of a whole month at sea, said a single word to him.

"Ay, well, ma name's Eenoo, lad. Eenoo McLennan, and Ah come frae Dundee in Scotland."

Muhesh looks puzzled and his eyebrows draw together in concentration as he struggles to decipher some recognizable sounds amongst the cacophony of vowels and glottalstops. When his dark forehead clears, his smile becomes a cavernous laugh, escaping from a hole in the center of his bony skull. Teeth, broken and protruding at all angles, appear for the first time.

"Sahib, I know Dundee!" he exclaims after a lengthy pause. "Many of my cousins and uncles have been to Dundee. They are sailors and take jute to your mills. The Verdant Works, the Eagle Mill, the Manhattan Works! Tay Spinners!" He recites the names of the unknown edifices like an excited child, then lowers his voice reverentially, "Do you own these mills, Sahib? You must be a rich man! Why is such a rich man traveling by train without servants? Why has the chauffeur not been sent to fetch you? But, excuse me, I have seen many British people, but I have never heard a name like yours. Is it a high-caste name, Sahib?"

Eenoo laughs out loud and claps Muhesh on the back, so that he staggers, much as the Welsh coal-master did to him in the bar of the *Narkunda*.

"Ah'm afraid the answer tae both o' yer questions is no, Muhesh! Ah'm no a mill-owner, Ah'm a mill-worker, a tenter. Ah work wi the weavers, lookin after the looms. An mah name's an Inuit name. Ma mother wus an Eskimo an ma faither wus a Dundee whalerman."

Still straining to catch the meaning, Muhesh repeats Eenoo's pronunciation of the word "*Inuit*."

"In-oo-it. I have never heard this word before, Sahib."

"She wus an Eskimo. Nanou, her name wus, frae Baffin Island, in the Arctic Circle, an ma faither stayed wi her family fer five year after he wus shipwrecked. Her faither an brothers rescued him frae the ice. Lost a foot wi the frost-bite. They cut it aff wi a flensin-knife. The cold froze his blood, they say. Then he brought Nanou an me an ma wee sister back tae Scotland, but the both o them died o influenza before they reached Aberdeen. So Ah wus brought up by ma faither an ma Gran. Ma Gran wus working on the weaving-flats frae six I' the mornin' tae six at nicht, an never off the feet. When the Great War started he wusn'a fit tae sign up wi the Black Watch, so he stayed in the hoos tae be a kettle-boiler, as they cried such men as didna work and couldna gang tae the war. Sometimes he'd stand on the shore an' he'd stare oot ower the wa'er fer an age, an Ah'd ask him how he wus takin sae lang, an he wouldna answer. Ah think he wus thinkin aboot ma mother an ma sister, lyin uner the sea; but he never said."

Muhesh is standing silently, his head still on one side. Eenoo's words wash over him like a bow-wave and fall untouched by interpretation onto the gritty platform behind him. In the distance, a noisy crowd of men is making its way, chanting, towards the station gates, and Muhesh turns to watch the turbaned gang as they wave and shout and jeer at passing cars.

"Eenoo, Sahib, I think you should go to the waiting-room now. It is at the other end of the platform. I will show you the way. But please come quickly, Sahib!"

Eenoo follows the tiny figure, whose hurpling gait puts him in mind of his father as he hobbled along with his false boot, woven from strips of whale skin and sealskin by Nanou and her mother in their Baffin Island igloo. When they reach the relative calm of the waiting-room, Muhesh turns and takes Eenoo by the wrist, pulling him through the door.

"I am not allowed to stay here, Sahib", he whispers, looking anxiously behind him, "but you must sit here until the danger is past. These men wish to free India from the British. They have come here to await the arrival of the train from Ishapore. They are waiting for the Viceroy, Sahib. They are supporters of the Congress and they will not be happy to see British people like yourself. I am most sorry to tell you, Sahib."

As Muhesh speaks, a train wheezes into the station and clanks to a stop opposite the station-master's office. The station-master, a greasy, irritable man, shuffles along a threadbare red carpet towards the first-class carriage with an air of self-importance and bows low as a tall, aristocratic-looking European in a white toupee steps out onto the platform. The volume of noise from the crowd at the gate rises to a crescendo with fanatical howls of "Hind Jai! Hind Jai!" and "Nehru! Pandit Nehru! Hind Jai!" Angry fists wave in the direction of the European, and punch the vibrating air like boxers. The Viceroy, followed by his retinue of impassive Indian servants, hesitates imperceptibly, then strides along the red carpet towards the gate, ignoring the din of the jostling men as they begin to surge forward into his path.

"What's goin' on Muhesh? What are they shoutin' aboot?"

Eenoo cowers behind the door of the waiting-room, the only other occupants of which are a European woman and a sallow-faced girl of eighteen or nineteen. An Indian servant hovers at the door. When they hear the roughness of Eenoo's accent, they exchange a doleful glance and lower their eyes to the books they are reading. The servant steps forward and gestures to Muhesh to move away. Muhesh does not move, but whispers loudly to Eenoo.

"These men are followers of Mahatma Gandhi, Sahib. He is the Living soul of India! And Mr Pandit Nehru, the President of the National Congress, Sahib. They wish the British lo leave India and India to become two nations. There have been many riots in Calcutta, and many soldiers to stop them. I have seen them. But I do not want you to leave, Sahib. Please do not leave, you are my friend. Just wait here and I will go and see what is happening. I will come back soon, I promise."

Muhesh limps away into the crowd which has gathered to see the action. The Viceroy has not yet reached the gate when the barrier gives way and the chanting hoard spills out onto the red carpet. From nowhere, police with batons and soldiers in puttees charge onto the platform and two shots ring out among the rioters. Eenoo stands transfixed as he sees Muhesh's spindly legs dragging along the ground and his small body being hauled through the station gate by uniformed thugs, a trail of dark blood staining the earth behind them. His eyes turn briefly towards Eenoo before he disappears into the throng. Eenoo moves forward to follow, but a hand on his arm restrains him and he turns around. It is the Indian servant from the waiting-room.

"I would not attempt to do what I think you are about to do, Sahib. A boy such as this is not worth the trouble. He was a foot-path dweller in the pay of followers of the Congress party and would die soon, in any case. Look, he has dropped his bag of cheap ornaments. Take them, they are worthless. You can do nothing, Sahib. Believe me."

For a long time, Eenoo sits in numbed silence in the waiting-room. Waves of nausea break over him as he tries to make sense of the extraordinary events of the past half-hour, as if he has walked by mistake into someone else's house and has witnessed an incomprehensible act of private violence. He looks down at the rough jute pouch the servant thrust into his hand and pulls at the twine which is holding it closed. As the bag falls open, an aroma of scented wood rises from a jumble of tiny, exquisitely woven baskets, each with a closely-fitting lid. It is the smell of sandalwood. Closing his eyes, Eenoo gently runs his fingers over each work of art created by Muhesh's mother, the blind weaver of dreams, while the two women stare out of the dusty window.

One Rite of Passage
Hannatu Green

IN MOST AFRICAN CULTURES, a child is initiated into rites of passage at the very tender age of five. A rite of passage in Africa does not always mean circumcisions, tribal markings, or tattoos. Thus, my story.

As a little girl, I remember doing almost everything with my mother. But when it came time for me to face the world, I had to do it all by myself. From dusk to dawn, from work to play, I was never idle. I was trusted, and the more chores I was given, the more I became responsible. I washed dishes and swept our compound under my mother's watchful eyes.

At daybreak, I comfortably put my first basket of *Kosai* on my head, bid my mother good-bye and took off into the world of business to sell my *Kosai*. It is also widely known as *Akara*, a popular Nigerian delicacy made with black-eyed peas.

At sunrise, I had covered most of my neighborhood. From door to door I called out to one and all. "Come on out and buy my mother's hot and delicious *Kosai*." Sometimes I was called into homes, but most times, everyone came out to buy.

It was a good day and a good start. I sold every single *Kosai* including my share. I carefully counted the coins to make sure they matched the number of *Kosai* my mother had given me. I was excited and felt proud.

At midmorning, I joined my grandmother at the local Adult Education Center where I learned to write my name in sand. After lunch, I happily set out again to market with a tray of fruits from my grandmother's orchard.

At sunset, we ate dinner. And as the moon brought out its natural brightness with the hidden mystery of the night, I joined other children for stories told by the elders. Afterwards, we danced, played games, shared riddles and jokes.

The night always ended with a word of wisdom and prayers from an elder. And so I enjoyed the journey into my rites of passage, instilling and building a purpose in life.

The Palace of Nansi
Dean Lawson

IT'S ADVERTISED AS A ROMANCE. The poster shows a Sudanese woman with a child at her side collecting gum from Acacia trees. An Usher shuts the lobby doors. Lights dim. Curtains divide. You see grains of sand begin to swirl and assemble. Soon the entire theatre is in the midst of this maelstrom. Hysterical laughter sweeps through the auditorium. Sand! In your hair, your eyes, your mouth, your nose. You squint and cover up with both hands - someone panics and shouts, Stop! Fade in: Shot of a truck's wheel, black and dusty with no cap; earth, dead and dry, caked on. Then the image of a soldier, climbing atop an ivory flatbed truck. A small girl in braids, with cheeks like pillows holds the leg of her mother. The Mother says there is a key for everything. She stands behind, cupping the child's eyes as the truck pulls away. Then says, *God says so.*

Chapter Six
Pilgrimage to Mount Kailash

The Rat
Frank J. Hutton

IT WAS A BLUE MORNING at the edge of Lake Superior. Cool and breezy, the air stung with freshness. We'd finished breakfast and cleaned up, a perfect time to take a seat. A couple of yards beyond our tent, the land pitched straight down a hundred feet and met the shore of the freshwater sea with only hard rock in between. I was content to sit comfortably at camp and look out over the water from this vantage.

Chipmunks crisscrossed the worst of the precipice, small enough to make a sure trail where we found only the most treacherous footing. They darted through camp to raid each promising spot and claim some piece of valuable scrap we didn't even know we'd missed. They were shameless beggars and sometimes came right up to us, looking for a handout, then streaked away when anything startled them. This was a battle well and fully lost. We routinely carried unsalted nuts for these little friends. They filled their cheeks until puffed like furry balloons, then ran off to secure their treasure for a later hour of need.

I was looking out over the lake when a short movement at the edge of the cliff caught my attention. I focused on the spot and watched a creature cautiously peak its nose above the rim. I'd never seen a healthier rat.

Here was no over-bred clump of whiteness living for rat chow or the lab technician's knife. Neither was this the black scourge of history, stealthy and disease ridden, stealing the plague and darkness into our lives. This little critter was alert as a bird and clean as a house cat. Tawny brown, almost yellowish, its bright pink nose wrinkled with the air, which sent shivers down its whiskers to read the breeze. As a boy, rats scared me because I'd had my share of surprise encounters with vile looking rodents. I sat still.

The rat was fully engaged and soon relaxed, for I posed no threat. It sat up on its hindquarters and proceeded to carefully clean itself, taking due time to assure its smooth fur was immaculate. It glistened in the morning sun. I watched the little fellow's tongue and paws work every inch of its plump body. After a while, the rat turned its back to me and disappeared down the hill from where it had come.

I should have known. I did know and was still surprised. There's nothing intrinsically evil or unwholesome about any wild thing. It is what it is and all that it is remains well outside civilized perception. Whatever moral or esthetic character we may choose to ascribe to any animal is us trying to define the world only through the narrow prism of vanity. I'd supposed I knew the rat. I'd thought it a scurrying, nasty beast with gleaming red eyes and aggressive disposition. I'd bought in to human nightmare.

The visitor at camp reminded me that it was we who made the rat of our fears.

Winter Storm
Elsie O'Day

red-streaked dawn, sailors warning, tilted and lost
to the surly menace climbing the eastern sky,
retreated behind the dense grey shroud whose belly
sagged low, horizon to horizon.

*no wind blew yet.

seagulls beat their raucous way in from shore,
settling uneasy in fields, lawns, on roofs.
early on I read the weather signs and hastened to fill
lamps with oil, count candles, ladle hearty stew
into thermal carafes; tea and coffee as well
and dropped a bag of seeds beside the kitchen door.

*birds will need food.

the first tentative flakes fell, melting as they
touched earth; I watched them… soft, pretty things,
as you carried arm loads of split, dry wood to fill the rack
and covered all with a tarp to keep it dry.
inside, more wood and a fire, kindling-laid.

*against power outage.

wind began its keening moan, bringing the smell
of salt air, the hoarse urgent shouts of unseen fishermen
securing boats in the choppy harbor with the swift
confident skill born of long years on the sea.
snow falling thickly now, blown by hard-driving wind.

*the blizzard settles in.

daylight swiftly withdrew, became a sullen gloaming,
silent except for the harsh sibilance of wind and snow,
children long since hallooed indoors, protesting.
full well we knew the danger of this storm, nor'easter,
yet still we lingered on the deck in stinging flying snow.

*swiftly accumulating inches.

it's time we shelter now, you said, so we turned indoors,
secured the cabin door, dropped the wooden bar across it.
hot stew and biscuits by lamp light, tea by a slow warm fire.
clothed in flannel, we piled the padded window seat with
pillows, tucking down comforters snugly around us.

*visibility zero.

no whine of plows growled through the drifted roadways.
abandoned cars. neighbors welcomed stranded motorists,
white shivering ghosts until they shed coats and boots
and gratefully accepted mugs of steaming stew,
absorbing the heat of the wood stove, toes on the hearth.

*snow is level with window sills.

fitful sleep interrupted by cracking, splintering tree limbs,
we aimed a flashlight out to check the depth of snow,
refilled the stove, talk desultorily for a while
then sleep again, in the safety of familiar arms,
the shrieking wind an eerie lullaby. hours passed.

Senryu
Jeff Haas

Enrico Fermi
Like wayward Prometheus
Stole fire from the gods.

The Afterlife, Ten Minutes
Shanna Karella

Open this box. See the stretch
of wasted limb, fingers and lip
curled on themselves—as if
some secret is held, in mouth
or palm—and the lie of waiting.
Roots have begun—tender purchase
found in soft folds, fertile soil's
mere proximity sensed through
thin space—and now we see: this husk,
a seedpod ripe and ready, is neither
fruit nor terminus, but both.

Eons have passed since the close
of lid, or minutes

    split by no word,
yet new life arrives, mere moments
from now, bursting up from below
or falling, as a gift from heaven.

Senryu: hummers
Elsie O'Day

nectar filled feeders
mist from sprinkler spurting high
birds of paradise

On the Road to Robbers' Roost
Robert Hampton

in the flint hills where the road to robbers'
roost meets then zig-zags east and then northward
away from the old santa fe trail, lime
hill stone chiseled respectfully upright
stands bearing the name of one left behind
during the play that was called westering.

down the road to robbers' roost, where the house
housing heisters counting their bank-mined loot
has been replaced by baled straw in large rolls,
where, bordering the field to the east trees—
hickory, sycamore, and walnut—stand
above sapling sticks and tangled brush, where
quail and pheasant and prairie chicken
perch, there: a soy bean field runs up the next
hill and toward the summit of blue stem
grass where a hidden pond ripples like sounds
playing back old conversations of bass.

the locals come here to hunt the upland
game and to claim their allotment of deer,
unaware the hunter is hunted too
where the road to robbers' roost returns
one to the old santa fe trail ribboned
across flint hill crests and, stopping once here
where the road from robbers' roost zig-zags
right, passing a lone chiseled stone before
soundless as a windy gravel born road
moving to the west then leaving the trail
south to the town where the cows go to die.
so the farmers pass and the ranchers pass
by bye and bye, and hunters hunting hope
within scope of a scope that is shaking
with each breath pass by bye and bye thinking,
here is the answer to death. the great herds

were important, you know, and worth saving:
the vast and sacred forms that the winds blow;
and they too were dissected by westering.

here: stand here by this lime stone head stone stand,
and face west where the next hill hides the sun,
while there is still adequate light for one
as the gravel trail runs over the ridge.
consider the killing done and to do
before the west turns back to east again.
consider how harmony comes, not new
as a store bought item from compromise
transactions while base line actions accrue,
but represents the absence of malice
and the triumph of innocence in you.
do not believe the things that they tell you.
stand here; before this lime stone stand and see
that balance is the way of things normal;
that there is no excuse for bad manners;
that everything follows its nature once;
that there are some doomed to repeat themselves;
that the only hell is repetition;
that the only crime is interference;
that there is no west; there is only east
and the countless variations thereof.
so where a farmer's wife or a rancher's
wife or phantom woman passes by
bye and bye placing flowers on the lime
stone stand, the wind implies voices through grass
strands. they should not have killed the buffalo,
you know, and with them America's hope,
not to mention the elk and antelope,
and the panthers leaving invisible
impressions in the weaving, changing strands.
shadow herds are streaming over yonder
hills towards this place with the grave stone face;
they cover the crests of the hills like moss
bringing back the aborigine dead.
on the road to robbers' roost to the north,
perhaps perched above the season's last straw,
an owl gives a hoot. yesterday, today,
or tomorrow a son and father watched
watch or will an eagle circling over.

now, but for the hill and wind, all is still.
did the will of the one left behind
here immediately stop pretending,
or did she run toward the last wagon
ambling to the west over the sunset
hill crying: mother, mother do not leave?
did she exit the land of make believe?

perhaps she stayed a while to assemble
the rudiments of perception that all
the time were there within her signaling;
and to understand that this lime stone stand
strewing the wind in a way it never
was strewn housed the same: one with a human,
therefore divine soul, and one with a name.
now, being free of preoccupations
with illusion and confusion, perhaps
she decided to let the wagons go.

perhaps she waited for the buffalo.
perhaps she said: i can leave when i leave?
and this is not the land of make believe?
on the road to robbers' roost coyotes
howl yapped cadences in the moon calmed hills.
the stars are so plentiful and bright that one
is among them; and when the eastern sky
brightens different from any other dawn
as all dawns are there are awakenings.
one knows then that this is the only day.
the pheasant fly from their roosts in the trees
as the sun warms their wings to their feeding.
somewhere a crow calls there should be a law.
deer move about saying please excuse us.
endless coveys of quail sun in bean fields
moving among the prairie chicken priests.
the bass works the pond like a magician.
doves coo gathering gravel at the corner
where the santa fe trail passes a lone
lime stone because this is where it happened.

Presque Isle
Frank J. Hutton

AUTUMN IS FULL UPON THE GROUND. Burnished bronze through faded gold are fallen, ragged at the edges, tumbled by the wind, season and spirit unbound.

Pressed by accumulation, resonance withers and smells of cascading time. Repelled at the scent of decay, the whisperers of the woods are silent—entreaty saved for ears more fresh with inclination to listen. Water running over rock murmurs. With winter just over the crest of tomorrow, effort granted the sleeping now would prove ill spent later, when darkness runs long and flow turns cold. Only the wind retains full voice, chilled even from the west and never silent. It roars, subsides, gains deep breath and rises fresh to throw a thin veil of grey across an otherwise radiant afternoon. The sun dims in acknowledgment. Long shadows mark the land, no matter midday.

Buzzards ride updrafts, alert to failed spirit and the prematurely fallen. They crane on the fly to look straight through thinning forest, down to the moist maze of color at its floor. Nothing stirs there but death on the breeze. The great black birds with dried blood heads peel off upon a gust, soaring sideways to the south and richer fields. In a moment, they are not even black dots against the sky.

That is not so easy to do, when one has no wings.

Once, we knew how to fly, or thought so anyway and the two are not so far apart as to determine critical distance. We drew full the nuances of autumn and soared upon its scent. As time seemed our own, we were free to call death arbitrary.

Then the future was whole with the past, Janus-faced and vibrant. Acute awareness made us weightless and at liberty to soar. If a salamander lived in the fire pit, the great owl stood guard at the gate and an otter grumbled with disdain at our foolishness, we knew the ways those signs pointed. And in a moment, we were not even black dots against the sky.

History outweighs promise and the ground is nearer than it ever was. Perhaps time makes that necessary, prerequisite to intimate relation. Flight becomes forgotten, lest memory prompt sad dreams and the burden of regret, acid of old age and slayer of spirit.

Autumn is full upon the river. Slow black water hosts a semblance of day across its face, to mask a heart gone cold. The reflection is as real as real, but right side down, heaven overturned. Only the gentlest ripple betrays presence as a canoe slides through the sky. Clouds part before the bow, pass on in silent moment and reform with a shiver, left behind. Blue pierces darkness and little fish seek the warmth of that light, unmindful of exposure. Occasionally, slender green stretches float upon the sky, waving slightly in revealed rhythm.

At its center of gravity, the world meets itself, the injury of distinction healed. Stones hover, weightless. Grasses weave in every direction. Forest rises from forest, to reach toward clouds above and below. The wind points nowhere.

A great heron rises from the water. A wide, slow arc is made across two skies before the bird comes to rest again downstream, near to where recall resides. Memory may be writ large, but actuality often disdains to contain it. What once was a torrent is now a trickle, distance is squeezed and callow courage has long since been tamped down by ongoing perspective. It's not that memory lies. In its time the moment was true and so remains. There the dead thing was, life reduced to muck and ooze. Decision was required by determination and two souls joined forever in headlong daring that was only just sufficient to the risk. The woods were thick, the trail obscure and blazed with fortitude. Memory is a stain, indissoluble. If the size of it does not fit the present, it is only that history has grown so large as to make the past seem small.

The day turns late. It's no trouble to move upstream. Only occasionally does current coax to the side. That's easily corrected with a bit of will and a gentle push. A pair of tiny ducks leads the way. Their delicate, duplicate forms effortlessly maintain safe distance.

An otter appears, its smooth fur throwing river on the rise. The distinction of time fades further. If it scolded for temerity, convergence would be complete, old acquaintance made fresh, the past resurrected. Instead, the beast is playful and curious. Repeatedly, it dips behind the clouds and then reappears to make inquiry with a delicate, complex string of melodic chirps and whirs. A slipstream in the sky leaves trace of its underwater path. Then the otter is gone. As happened long ago, in a heartbeat unnoticed, an invitation seems to have been withdrawn, a secret offered unbidden, then withheld. Now history augments flight and seasons come undone. The world known to otters and that familiar to men intersect. History is irrelevant. The present is a promise that can be forsaken, never broken. Knowledge is no more excuse than ignorance.

Wisdom is an intimate nation, separate from illusions of transience and corporeal concern. Autumn is full upon me. Flight upriver is leisurely. Air and water are one. Earth is indivisible and firelight streams through all. The nuance of place and moment is reflected whole in the richness of the season. All around, schools of little fish leap, fall back and leap again. Golden leaves sway gently in the breeze and the river runs as deep as heaven is high. Night is at the horizon, with winter just beyond. Steady against the current, the high sun of summer left forever behind, flying proves instinctive.

From this vantage, it's plain that the first bright star of evening will find its proper place upon the water and be cast back to the sky, as once was the midday sun.

Senryu
Jeff Haas

I see your penchant
for global self-destruction
and raise you a poem.

Chapter Seven
Justice Hung In the Balance

Justice
Ajay Prasannan

When Crazy Horse Ran the Gauntlet of Guns
Robert Hampton

crazy horse still rides in front of the fire
lining like burning darts from the soldiers'
guns across the chosen path of one
they called the strange one. some of the bullets
rifle through his great mane of flowing hair
as long and as wide as four alexander
helmets, and, embraced by the strands
of time, space and continuum, braided
for a wisp of air, they fall harmlessly
away; some are like bees in his horse's
ears; some of the bullets about to strike
suddenly meet rushing air that vacuums
them away, confusing the marksmen's minds.

when crazy horse passed in front of soldiers'
guns, he followed the same path in four ways
apparent only to the great spirit
and the one called crazy horse. some bullets
were exhausted before they reached their
mark and bounced off like off of superman.
some soldiers did not want to hit their mark,
when the strange one called crazy horse passed four
times, as if from four different directions
at once, converging at the center then
darting in unison to the circle's edge.
some soldiers must have asked if all these
men called savages were as brave as this
one, who rides like a ghost rider riding.

when crazy horse teased at the soldiers'
guns, and revealed the soldiers' positions,
he saw, it is said, some of the bullets,
and it is true they have names, but the names
are not real, yet close enough to fool one
to death. his name was not on any, it

is said he said. medicine men of strong
medicine meditated until their
liberation on the wings of crazy
horse's ride; and the children are soaring
still. earth, it is said, will not persecute
her beloved ones, and, sometimes, her love
spins like an energy shield around one
while hot thoughts whirl like bullets around one.

when crazy horse ran the gauntlet of guns
positioned side by side with limited
lateral movement, the sound of horse hooves,
the only ones in the world, created
the illusion of reality
when crazy horse ran the gauntlet of guns.
when crazy horse proved that time is not real,
that there is the moment and the moment
only, allowing each of the watching
warriors to choose a personal moment,
then, as with all great moments, time was still
when crazy horse proved that time is not real.
crazy horse still rides in front of the fire
rifling through his great mane of flowing hair.

Crazy Horse and His Band of Oglala
Sketch by Mr. Hottes

A Million Todays (Rachmaninoff,
Prelude No 12 G# minor, Opus 32)
Ivan Gabriel Rehorek

It is only the chill of Death we bear
as the morning dew trembles in the sun
sad eyed as old calendars
days of yore and Valkyrie nights
where we used the moon for a skipping stone
and drew hopscotch with the stars

it is only chilled breath, we're aware
as the day the only day back flips and cartwheels
whirling thru' the sepia waltz
falling in love but getting up again—
ah, but they're just old wounds and attitudes
seen thru' another half-wit night

it is a lonely, still dread in there
as mid-day is gone, far gone
the sun keeps bravely on
as daylight fades into grey
gather your children under the polluted sky
they've been picking stars and dandelions
and is it only your will that makes you care?

For there're a million todays and all the angels are playing
marbles and poker with all the devils
Columbus and Baron Munchausen engrossed in chess,
and look there, Dad!

Can you see the dinosaurs and unicorns, there?
So the hour has spilled and time is everywhere
twinkling in the darkened forests—
every day we must be children.

Flowers in her Cheeks
Katherine Elizabeth Kennedy

IN THE COURSE OF MY WORK, multiple cups of tea and lengthy conversations, I gained the trust and confidence of Iraqi officers. As our friendships deepened I felt more freedom in sharing my personal thoughts and not just those of the army. This was my second deployment to an area in which I was the only white female. On one particular night, the only Christian national in the group rose to greet me and shook my hand. The rest nodded and said, "Touch you after dinner."

Conversations with the Iraqis often turned to the difference between Muslim and Christian faiths or Iraqi and American cultures. This night was no exception. The officers were quick to point out the hypocrisy of Christians in America, but failed to identify their own shortcomings.

"It is dishonorable how Americans marry and divorce, marry and divorce," one Iraqi colonel said.

"According to your religious custom you can have up to four wives. After you tire of one, you add another. Not much difference," I said.

An Iraqi lieutenant colonel switched the conversation to greed. "Americans are immoral and greedy; they don't care about anyone else and only do what is best for themselves."

"Oh, and stealing fuel and food from your unit to take home on leave is okay?" I asked.

"Yes, you don't understand. Saddam used to give his commanders gifts; these are all things we deserve. He gave us everything we needed and now we have no food or fuel with which to cook, heat our homes, or buy vehicles."

"Didn't it make you mad that he had all those palaces?" I asked.

"We couldn't speak out against it, but he did take care of us to some extent and now we are scraping by."

"Scraping by. You have a $250 phone."

"Oh, but I need this phone," he said.

Iraqis, in many ways, are no different than Americans, living beyond their means, having many wives.

The two years I spent in Iraq, I witnessed the worst of mankind coinciding with immense generosity. There is no perfect answer for ending war; there is only the insistence of a universal standard of right and wrong.

Nations will continue to go to war, but those involved in conflicts need to pause a moment and notice. It may be something as simple as a flower making its way out of a pile of rubble or a baby laughing as it bounces on its mother's knee. War will exist.

While I was there, one of the Iraqi soldiers wrote a poem to me right before I left for home. Names have been changed in places and deleted to protect the innocent, and a simple excerpt of the longer work is provided here. The words are the ones he spoke and recalls our first meeting.

"When Captain Kennedy comes into the headquarters and into the hallway with the yellow ceiling, I see a human being come in, there is no power, but there is a light shining. Oh, for the dove shines. She is sitting with the transportation officer. I focus intently on the interpreter because I do not understand her speech. Her words are foreign; they are not Arabic, they are not Kurdish. There is a light, but there is no power. The interpreter tells me that he does not understand Captain Kennedy's words and that he needs another interpreter to translate for me.

I tell the interpreter that I need him to be patient. I am from Nasira: the boat city, a lovely city, with a date tree on the bank of the river.

This situation we are talking about is no big deal. I tell her that she is lovely, even if she did not know that I am from the south; from the center of Nasira. There, I say, I saw a beautiful flower and there are a lot of these flowers in her cheeks. There are officers around her in the meeting: Captain S, a brother; Captain A, from maintenance; and Captain H. Captain H. wants something and she only answers him a little bit. I am still asking about whom this lady is, in the maintenance room with the yellow ceiling, and she answers, "The person with the golden hair is the American, Captain Kennedy."

Footprints in the Jungle
Oral Testimony, Neng Xiong

"TIME IS MEASURED IN SORROW beyond the count of days. My Hmong people are starving and eating tubers and roots in the jungles of Laos afraid to return to their village, yes, today, thirty years after the Viet Nam war. The Laos government drops flyers from airplanes asking my people to come back to the villages. They say, "You will be safe." Within a few days, Laos and Vietnamese surround my people, their homes and farms, torture and kill them, so many children die.

No one can see our shredded hearts or hear our cries for help. The United Nations says there is too much fighting everywhere. This is just a skirmish, a small civil war in Laos.

Some Hmong flee to Thailand this year (2009), but the Thai government refuses to let new Hmong refugees stay. They say, "You Hmong have come to Thailand illegally. Go home." And then the Hmong are killed when they go back to Laos.

There used to be one hundred thousand Hmong hiding in the jungles of Laos. Now, we think only about seventeen thousand are still alive, but it is hard to know. It is too dangerous for my Hmong people to return to their farms without help. The United Nations can watch this; provide help for Hmong until they can be part of Laos again. Time and time again, the Vietnamese and Laotian governments kill them. My people must run and hide all the time—in the jungle— moving every two weeks, so many dead, so little food, or they will be found. The government soldiers follow their footprints, their abandoned huts. Soon, only footprints and shadow spirits will be left.

What Reason Does a Mother See in War
Robert Hampton

what is one to say your son the soldier
died as a soldier that politics stirred
the melting pot and he followed orders

what reason does a mother see in war

what shall one say he did his duty ma'am
it was one of those things that transpire
when soldiers are at risk in perilous fire

what method of speech what correct parlance
shall one say your son ma'am was the bravest
man i have known and he died a hero

where is the comfort in something she knew
long before the car opened and soldiers
with somber steps ascended the steep stairs

long before this child they call a soldier
she knew the child whom they called a soldier
the qualities of late discovered say

here is what he was what he represents
but that is not the full truth far from it.
mothers see beyond these recognitions

perhaps she will say i know you must do
your duty but know that my son was born
a hero and was a hero before.

Mort pour la France
Townsend Walker

I SEE YOU'RE LOOKING AT THE OBELISK in the center of place de Verdun, here in Fountaine. I thought they would've done a better job; used marble perhaps. But there wasn't much money after the war. People did what they could. Lucien, the carpenter, was only an apprentice and it shows. He shaped up the obelisk in wood, and then poured in the concrete.

See the plaque at the base of the obelisk, there, on the side facing the church. Forty names under the heading *Mort pour la France (Died for France)*. I'm in the middle, Emile Duprés. Right there between my brothers Charles and David, and above Henri and Leon, my cousins. No one remembers the Duprés family now. The war to end wars ended our family. Since then no one has stopped long enough to hear the story. Stay a while.

Forty men on this plaque; that's a lot for a small village. When the war broke out in '14 there were seventy men here. Forty-five went out; five came back. The ones that came back weren't the ones people wanted to come back. War doesn't choose that way.

It's not on the plaque, but I was the only one from the village who was an officer. The lieutenant in charge of our platoon was killed; I could read and write, so I was made lieutenant. Someone had to read the orders, and write back and confirm them. The war was conducted according to its rules. Generals, fifty miles from the front line, wrote orders. They sent them to colonels and captains twenty miles away, who sent them to lieutenants. The orders were always the same, *Charge the enemy.* We weren't people there on the front line; we were ammunition thrown out on the battlefield. And the battlefield took what it wanted—arms, legs, whole bodies. We had a war everyone said was glorious.

My parents were proud to have an officer in the family. For the first time my father was able to look the mayor and priest in the eye. Christine was proud, too. She was able to tell everyone that her son's father was an officer. It didn't help little Nicolas get any money after the war though. She wasn't able to prove I was his father. We'd been in a hurry.

Being an officer didn't mean much. It only hurried the end. When I led the charge on the Boch trenches the day after Christmas there was an explosion, then fire, and I was inside the fire.

Senryu
Jeff Haas

A swirling black hole,
Pulling me ever downward
Toward oblivion.

Just another lullaby
(on a train to Auschwitz)
Alex Braverman

Sleep dear baby,
grow in your sleep,
close your eyes. Maybe
we should count sheep.

You'll be a doctor
or a musician,
a famous conductor,
a noble physician.

> No mama, no. I'll be a gravedigger.
> Corpses to respect me,
> crows to protect me,
> earth to hide me,
> worms to find me.
> Where we are going—there's no job bigger.

One for the master,
one for the dame…
Let no disaster
harm you or maim.

You'll be a Rabbi,
Moisheleh dear,
listen to lullaby,
banish your fear.

> No mama, no. Your words are phony.
> The Serpent bit Moses,
> Abraham dozes,
> time was frozen,
> we were chosen.

And when I grow up—will you call me Johnny?

Shuh! little treasure,
rest in your sleep.
Adonai will measure
what should man reap.

Black Hole
Kyle Hemmings

I am beyond Megatron or
stars burning your kilowatt desires,
I spin and spin
and my escape velocity
exceeds your capacity for guilt,
for I have none,
anything that passes me
I suck in and devour:
galaxies of friends, family members,
even explorers who deny
the eternity of my chasm,
I turn everything into nothing,
then, nothing into something.
I am not a black hole
or a counter-proof against Newton,
I am merely God's darkest thought
that the inverse of creation
is someone's heart imploding
and through Him anything is possible.

Senryu: Secrecy
Elsie O'Day

Warm breath of summer,
Coaxing new life from the earth,
Masks the killing fields

The Poem That Isn't
Shanna Karella

about the remains we can see, half-choked
and sticking out of weeds and bushes
like legs escaped from a shroud;

or the fact there's no identifying marks
left tattooed into the skin, because
that's missing too, when suddenly

the line between German engineering
and a shady ditch along a dusty road,
or that no matter how hard we scrub

we're still covered in that horrid rust
of the guilty bystander, becomes awfully thin—
even though we weren't there then

we know the chrome salute of fear of being
different, and that we might have looked away
and mumbled *Heil, Heil* with all the rest.

Chapter Eight
Piacere Rubato: Stolen Pleasure

Going Up and Down the Stairs
Raquel Chalfi [Translator Tsipi Keller]

She teaches me not to be ashamed
of the chemistry of minutes   it's not a holy alchemy
it's a raw chemistry one can write poems about
she makes things with it
going up and down the stairs
of her consciousness with the trailing   train
of the useless poetry dress
she takes the emergency exit stairs
you'd think she's walking on a flat road and blows words
they won't hold onto her steep railing
I'll hold onto her railing so she won't slip
and will glide down
like a totally
demented girl

Senryu
Jeff Haas

Nietzsche once observed
"God is dead and we killed Him."
Nothing's been the same.

That Animal You
James S. Oppenheim

I like that animal you—
Your horse laugh
Pig tails, crow's feet,
Your sweet monkey's face
With which you de-lice my heart.

How Will My Love to My Heart
Be Calm by Becoming?
Robert Hampton

some days, and even some minutes of some
days, one asks: how will my love to my heart
be calm by becoming? will she become
the final confirmation of a bell?
if my love comes to me today,

will she come child
running among the geese of her knowing?

will she come treading through desolation
until the last foot fall on the last corpse
in chaos her lover?

will my love be coming like the gold
dawn or the fawn at the spring before dawn?

will my love becoming come masquerade
of the moment in the finest silks wrapped,
eternal beauty moving like a saint?
will she come faceless without eyes to paint?

will she come motionless except for heart
the appropriate mind for human kind?

will she come drifting like an errant weed
the infinite gypsy mother of seed?

will she come with her form disfigured, bent
or broken, scarred or torn? will she be gnarled
about her lips in a permanent frown with a
voice like a scolding crow and nerves
brittle as conscious pain will allow for life
as she speaks my name; as she speaks my name?

when she comes will she have cried all the tears
that the suffering in one life will allow?

some days, and even some minutes of some
days, one asks: how will my love to my heart
be calm by becoming? will she become
the final confirmation of a bell?

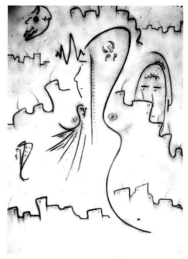

City Doodle
Dean Lawson

Old Old Magic

Ivan Gabriel Rehorek

Springtime leaps with blue and gold
they're spinning clouds that sing and dance
the road winds on like a chorus:
it's an old, old magic, this

that takes you by the hand
and with that first breath of music,
slides in under the skin.
Ah, it's an old, old magic, this.

All laughing and screaming now,
flipping coins like stars on high
and rolling eyes at the bedside moon—
it's an old, old magic, this:

the pillow-clouds roll on the minor theme
shuddering breaths of dreams,
but patient heartbeat sees it thru',
it's an old, old magic, this,

with a nod and a turn
it's an old old magic this—
another night sings out loud:
it's an old, old magic, this!

The Bicycle Thief of Le Nieppe
Kyle Hemmings

THE BOY, JEAN PIERRE, plodded towards the woman writhing off to the side of the pebbled road. His eyes trailed over her bike, a boy's bike. The long slanted bar stretched its frame, and the wheels, a mesh of jagged and punched spokes tilted at impossible angles in the air. The woman struggled to lift herself to one knee, arched her back and grimaced. Her face crinkled when she spoke, reminding him of the fine lines in a wine cork. He conjured a much younger woman, not much older than his mother, or like his mother: a woman with henna-colored bangs, a chin-length coiffure, gooseberry almond-shaped eyes that slanted and widened when she spoke. This woman looked nothing like his mother.

Her salt-and-pepper hair, pulled in a loose ponytail cut a jagged diagonal against her ears, shaped like a seashell. Her copper and flabby nose stretched above a line of cracked lips. The lips and nose seemed an odd couple, a marriage of convenience. Squinting, he could almost make out tiny veins that marked the inset of her cheeks.

"Can you hide me?" she said in a flat, demanding voice.

She stood and stumbled towards him. His legs stiffened; his arms tensed like the wings of a vigilant bird, ready to take flight.

* * * * *

He was certain it was her. He was certain it was the same woman, this bicycle thief, whom his mother and others gossiped about at street markets, an informant hunted by members of the *Gagoule* as well as the Germans. His fingers throbbed, and his eyes zigzagged over her wrinkled, smudged dress. A smell of cow skin and alpine forest wafted over, and he thought of brisk mornings rising over pastures, of lakes, thick and calm as sweet butter, and albino children bathing in the water. She was not from the South, he surmised, not from his village near Castries nor from Artes. The women there smelled of seawater and lemon. The women of *la mer*.

He imagined these women *dans le nord*, with long necks and crooked fingers, who sold fresh hens' eggs and spongy tomatoes for a quarter of their pre-war price. Off duty, (he heard through a hundred grapevines) they pedaled their bikes through Paris, delivering secret messages, women whose husbands convened in underground tunnels. Their faces had the same deadpan eyes and flattened lips as the bicycle thief's. He was certain it was she. Not so much certain as wanting to be certain, as if in a dream, an orange-hued dream.

Follow me, he said.

* * * * *

He pedaled his bicycle next to her as they went, twisting the handlebars to avoid large stones, or gaping holes in the road. Her silence stung him, teased him like the tart juice of strawberries that always made his skin itch. At times, she hobbled to keep pace.

"Is your leg broken?" he asked.

"Am I not walking?" she said. He waited for her to comment about his knobby knees, or his mismatched *chaussettes*. At least, he could pride himself about them not having holes, or as his mother called them, "tiny smiles." She said nothing.

The pebbled road soon forked into narrow cobblestone alleys, a loose row of mated village houses with open windows and rectangular beds of flowers. He pointed to his home. She must not stir in the house, he said, without looking back at her. He sensed she understood the sound of rabbit feet or cottontails.

When he reached home, he uncoiled a loop of old rope from a leather bag and tethered the bike to a flimsy black gate of iron lattice. They marched up the steps into his room. There, he pointed, you will stay in that closet. I will lock it, and you can only come out when I let you. He pointed to a hallway that smelled of old linen in open hampers. The bathroom is to the right, he instructed, and you must jiggle the chain three times, at least three, or it will not flush. It's a rusty chain and doesn't always work.

She turned to peruse the room and rarely blinked as he spoke. He lingered over her blanched face, drawn to it like a wishing well. He stopped speaking. Each stared into the others' face, perhaps, he thought, wishing each other's dreams. Her face hung gaunt, as the flesh around her cheeks tightened, as her mouth straggled, as if the idea hit her, as it did him, that she had not been granted sanctuary, but rather, had been made a prisoner by a fourteen-year old.

He rolled his eyes down and across while she kissed his cheek and thanked him. His words faded to a whimper, the trailing of a lullaby, like a breeze from the sea.

"It is inconvenient, I know."

"It will do." He cleared his throat, trying to summon the strength to ask a stranger to divulge a secret, one he already knew. He stammered, stopped and began again.

"And what does Madame do with all those bicycles she steals?"

Her eyes narrowed and her skewed jaw straightened. She turned, loped towards the closet, like some wounded animal, and closed the door. Jean Pierre stood there for a moment, imagined the sensation of walking on air, of having a body like a kite.

Remember, he preached, facing the closed door, you must move like an angel. He wondered if his words sounded muffled to her.

* * * * *

Over the weeks, he slipped plates of crusty bread and cheese under her door,portions from his own meals. He waited, sitting on the edge of his bed, for the empty plate to be shoved back. On some nights, he'd wake up, stifle his breaths, shuffle to the closet, and tap three or four times. He heard her rustle, then she'd return the same tap, the same number of times.

It became a daily ritual, this code, to verify she was not dead. Unlike the fisherman's wife, a demure woman no one suspected—Jean Pierre had witnessed her execution several weeks before. She was given no blindfold before being shot in front of a staggered line of townspeople that included her husband and two small sons.

He both cringed and rejoiced at this new power and the effort to sustain a choice: to either save his ideal of this woman or to starve her body. Behind that closet, she was larger than life. She was not an insect to feed crumbs. She was the bicycle thief from Le Nieppe who long before the war clasped her hands to her bosom and batted her eyebrows in silent films. One director, Jean Pierre's mother recalled, referred to her as "the girl with the buttermilk skin and hornets' nest eyes." Everyone remembered her films, but no one, his mother told him, had ever met her, or if they did, they would mistake her for a beautiful stranger they wished to resemble.

And there came nights when he floundered in a dream he could not locate himself in, wandering, searching for the nexus of village life, buried, hushed. He stood in the middle of a room with burnt umber walls, a house with no roof. From his window, he could see a chain of bicycle riders racing down the street. They stole his breath. There were faces he recognized from previous dreams, round-faced fleshy women laughing on red or white bicycles with double seats. They wore wide, floppy hats and their skirts ruffled in the downstream wind. Their eyes reflected the afternoon glide of swans, or the swoon of starving hummingbirds. Their eyes reflected the arms of their partners, audacious and amorous men, who refused to steer their bicycles in a controlled manner. In the night, he awoke and imagined her standing over him, imagined the sound of her pulse threading from her wrists to his ears, a swift unforgiving river forging through him.

She was not there.

He threw off his sheets and stood, gazing at the closet door for minutes.

* * * * *

Three times a week, a German officer, angular and chain smoking, younger than Jean Pierre's missing father, came to call. Gunther, his mother said, and he watched her eyes dance at his hobnailed footsteps up the path. He swung baskets of wine, sleepy bodies of smoked fish, long arms of dimpled bread. Around Jean Pierre, he blushed, and his own arms dangled useless as wind chimes on a stagnant day. His eyes twinkled a North Sea blue. Jean Pierre wondered what sort of fish, (herring? pilchard?) thrived in cold waters, and what kind of bait would one use. Surely, he thought, this man could teach him.

Sidling down the hallway in the middle of the night, Jean Pierre would press his ear to his mother's bedroom door and imagine the unfolding cusps of secrets, the rustle of undressing, the sail of voices like odd musical notes answering one another. He both wept and gritted his teeth. He wept over his mother's gift of offering herself to procure for them a steady basket of food. He wept over the way her voice would stay with him like a brooding cello in a Bach fugue. He gritted his teeth over Gunther's ability to play a woman like a cello.

Someday, Jean Pierre thought, he too would pluck the strings of women's bodies behind closed doors, and leave it to whoever was listening to weep.

When his father was in the house, there was only snoring and frequent argument over his infidelity. While Jean Pierre sat on a sagging bench in a park in late afternoon, he drew himself and Gunther in sketch books, riding bicycles. He did not know the German word for stepfather. He could fathom neither the temperature of the North Sea, nor the height of its rogue waves. He had heard the word Jutland uttered from his teachers' lips and with this he associated burning flesh, jettisoned pieces of ship metal, green patches of cemetery. On lazy afternoons, he pondered this. Summer lazy and he drew Gunther's eyes too large, the belly too protruding, much like that of his father, a man who loved patisseries and cream layered mille feuilles.

Then he would rise to greet his friend, a scrawny chestnut-eyed classmate named Marcel, and they stood facing each other, extending their arms, bending them into rigid contortions from the elbow. They would imitate the cryptic motions of British flagmen they once saw on behemoth destroyers with marvelously fluted hulls, iron mistresses off the coast.

"You're getting too good, Jean Pierre." Marcel dropped his arms.

"I wish I knew what they meant. My mother's friend could teach me."

"Can he teach me?"

And on nights following the German's departure, Jean Pierre would stuff the bicycle thief's plates with generous portions of meat and fish.

"Why so much?" she whispered from behind the door.

"Life is good sometimes," he answered, "so don't ask questions."

Then, after she slid the barren dishes back, he'd ask her again why she stole bicycles. "If I feed you," he said, "do me the courtesy of answering."

She said nothing.

He choked at her defiance. After formulating a strategy, he snuck full plates halfway through the door, withheld them, and told her that either she answer or would not eat. Again, she would say nothing. He pulled back the plate. The routine kept up for days. This power, both cruel and efficient, a power he envied in Gunther, backfired and caused Jean Pierre to stammer in his mother's presence, to look for socks that matched and despise anything resembling a tear, or a "tiny smile." He grew sleepless at the thought of the bicycle thief's puny form shriveling behind the door.

Then one evening, he knocked, slipped the plate halfway and repeated his question. Her voice cracked and wavered.

"I steal them for the children and mothers to flee to Switzerland."

"Do they reach the border?"

"I do not know."

"Does it bother you, Madame, that you send them to their deaths?"

"I merely give back to them—this gift of living."

"You think you can change bread into fish, Madame?"

He released the plate and imitated Gunther's hard stare at informants, as if this could have bored an irreparable hole in that sham door.

"Informants are fools," he said, "my father was a fool."

"Then why do you feed me? And pastries? Where do you get the pastries?" She spoke as she chomped food.

Be quiet, he told her. He tiptoed to the window and watched a small wave of soldiers goose step down the cobblestone street. Then, he skittered over to his old chest, pulled out a drawer, and held up two handkerchiefs. In the mirror, he watched himself practice those flagmen's signals, not knowing which meant what.

* * * * *

One morning, shortly after Jean Pierre's mother left to shop in the street markets, he tapped on the closet door. Silence. He tapped again, harder, until his knuckles reddened. He unlocked and swung open the door. There was not even a ghost of her.

He raced down the steps and searched for her in the streets. After spotting his mother negotiating with a bushy-mustached fruit vendor, he peered both ways, and dashed into a coiling side street. He found the bicycle thief traipsing in open daylight, babbling out loud, laughing while she held a cluster of cherries she must have stolen. He ran up and grappled with her.

"Madame, you must come back. The soldiers will kill us."

She pivoted one way and then the other. He shook her and said please. "I cannot take it. The room. The darkness. The dust."

"Please," he said.

"Suffocates me."

She grew a faint smile. He clutched her arm as if she meant something to him, something more than faded movie stars or women with painted birthmarks or those who cried fake tears.

"I will not stay long," said the bicycle thief.

With one of his handkerchiefs forming a loose knot at the back, he covered her head, and she followed him. She hummed songs he did not recognize.

* * * * *

The next morning, Jean Pierre twitched at the sound of a gathering commotion and sprung to his bedroom window. A small crowd of people and soldiers assembled in front of the house. His mother shook her head and made flamboyant leaps with her arms. Her yelling, he thought, could have reached the other side of the Mediterranean. She peered up and waved for him to come down. His heart began to knock. To the closet door he rushed, delivering the warning code: three light taps, a pause and one strong knock. Did she understand? There was not a stir. But he thought, even though he had no time to think, what did one expect to hear from an angel gathering behind a closet door?

He swiveled on his feet and ran towards the staircase. Down the steps he scrambled; ostrich feet, hoping for a body like a feather.

His mother, standing near her lover, fixed her gaze on a stoop-shouldered woman wrapped with a wool shawl, tapping the ground with a cane. The mother turned to Jean Pierre, curling her fingers.

"This woman, Jean Pierre, says she spotted the bicycle thief of Le Nieppe yesterday with you. They think we are hiding her." Jean Pierre's tongue turned to something heavy and unyielding: a chunk of wet sand. He shook his head to mean no, to mean he could not open his mouth.

"C'est absurde, non?" she said.

"I have never seen her."

"We will search the house anyway," said Gunther, nodding to his superior officer, then to the younger recruits. His abrupt and mispronounced diphthongs made Jean Pierre's stomach churn. His mother rolled the air with a flat-shaped hand. *"Je vous en prie."* Be my guest. Her face grew mottled and red. Gunther reached for a cigarette and steadied a silver lighter using both hands.

The soldiers led the way and Jean Pierre felt the urge to jump on his bicycle and ride to the sea. Would he be the first boy to swim to Algiers? Would he sink to the bottom of the ocean and dream of the bicycle thief in his last struggle for air? Would he blow bubbles and see the Madame's face reflected in them? The clopping of feet up the stairs made him hunger for kites and things not earthbound.

"There is no woman up there!" Jean Pierre screamed his little boy's shriek.

His mother swung around on the steps and put a finger to her lips. "Let them find out for themselves," she said.

In the hallway, Gunther instructed the group to split into two, one half to the mother's room, the other to the boy's. Jean Pierre watched his mother wince and rub a hand against her lower lip. In his bedroom, Jean Pierre stood behind the women, shuddering as the soldiers scoured his bedroom, ripped off sheets, flipped the mattresses, tore up floor boards—unlocked the closet. What excuses could he come up with? He didn't know it was her? Then why was he hiding her? Or he could say she was a homeless woman, a woman who had lost her mind, claiming she was this or that. He felt sorry for her and wished to protect her. He never believed she was the bicycle thief from the North. How could she have ridden so far? And who would care to prove a fourteen year-old boy wrong?

No, he thought, none of it would work. He would do better by spoon-feeding castor oil into their mouths. He would die with the bicycle thief. He would admit to everything. They would be executed together. They would die fools.

In the closet, the soldiers rummaged past his clothes, pounded their fists against shaved wood. One began prying apart strips welded by tiny nails. A crawlspace, he announced, but enough to fit someone. Jean Pierre stepped forward and brushed shoulders with the women. The old one with the cane would not look at him. Another, with blemished skin and horned glasses, scowled at him.

Standing on tiptoe, he eyed the soldier poking his stubby fingers behind the flimsy panels, squeezing his head through crevices of his own making. He could see the cellar, he yelled with a flick of the head, and could hear the scurrying of squirrels or perhaps a rat. Yes, a rat, most likely, he corrected himself. Gunther said to get on with it, a rat or a squirrel was of no import. The soldiers tore out more wood planks. The women yawned; the younger ones ogled Gunther. One flipped her wrist and rubbed the face of her watch.

Gunther huffed and clapped his hands once. "She is not here," he said. "We are finished."

He threw down his cigarette and flattened it with the toe of his boot. He ordered everyone out of the house. The two groups reconvened in the street.

The woman with the shawl and imperfect bun of hair, poked at the ground with her cane, shouted at Jean Pierre's mother.

"I saw her before! She stood at your son's bedroom window. The room we were in."

The mother stuck a finger to the side of her head and spun it.

"You are crazy, Madame. You are crazy. What will you tell me next? That my fourteen-year old is hiding Charles De Gaulle under his bed?"

"Your son is a liar."

Jean Pierre's mother lunged at the woman, striking her shoulders with the bottoms of her fists. Gunther and one other soldier broke them apart. The woman stooped to retrieve her cane. Rising, her face grew withered and cagey, a face old as sponges. His mother unloaded a tirade of curses, then spat in the street. Gunther directed a stern gaze at her. Several soldiers smiled and huddled, their hips loose, knees bent. Jean Pierre ran up and grabbed his mother's arm, pulling at the loose flesh of it until his thin hands shook from the strain.

She spun on her heels and slapped him with a wild undirected ferocity. His lips slipped apart and he started to cry, a deep ravenous cry, as if one was mourning the lack of water or spring. She grew hysterical and threw her arms around the boy's head, neck, pulling him to her chest, saying she didn't know it was him. She didn't mean it for him. He pushed her away, then took several clumsy steps back away from the group.

"You see," she said to the old woman whose back was turned, "you see what you made me do." The woman turned and crept towards Jean Pierre's mother until an inch from her face.

"Child, do you not sleep with a German? Does he not feed you?"

His mother's jaw froze and her eyes turned glassy.

The woman lumbered away, tapping the ground with her cane at irregular intervals. There was now a sanguine glow to her face, and Jean Pierre thought of someone dreaming of nesting sparrows.

The other women then dispersed, some shrugging, guffawing, others shaking their heads. To Jean Pierre, they shrunk to tiny dots in the distance, past the serpentine road to the beach. Jean Pierre's mother motioned him to come inside the house. He waved her away as if her apologies would only turn to poisoned fruits. Staring at the odd-shaped rocks in the road, she tottered back into the house, making no eye contact with Gunther. Jean Pierre stood still in the middle of the street. He could have stood there until nightfall if need be. He could have thought forever.

His head jerked.

Several distant shots rang out. He flinched. He froze. His lips pinched. He thought of her, or another informant like his father, the impact of a body hitting dirt, the lull of orange-hued dreams.

No dreams.

He trudged back to the house. He decided to wait. He decided she wouldn't die just yet. If it was she. Then, on bicycle, he would search for her, along the beach, along the calm sun-drenched littoral; she would be lying beside snails, picking up baby clams, opening her fingers and watching the sand trickle in free fall. She would be smiling and carrying an old tune. She would recall the men who once directed her in movies, and she would display uncanny insights into their philosophies, her affairs with them.

How weak men are, she would say, but she loved them anyway. She would promise Jean Pierre that someday she would show him old clippings of her when she was shapely as a recoiling whip and lucid as a cargo ship's helmsman. She would take him by the arm and claim they could dance on water, that the salt of the Mediterranean would hold them up. She would dance on the sand, spreading her arms that were her wings, and twirl and twirl in her loose satin and lace dresses, long and trailing. She would twirl until she became dizzy or she fell.

He stopped in front of his house. Was it a vision? Like the kind that occurred to the Maid of Orleans, he wondered? From the rail, the rope dangled loose; the tiny threads at the ends hung in loose waves. His bicycle was gone.

He climbed upstairs, ignoring his mother's pleas for him to come down. The walls vibrated with her shrill voice. He shut himself in the dusty closet and sank to its hard scuffed floor. He listened to her footsteps up the stairs, then stopping, more steps, then planting herself in front of the closet door. She jiggled the knob that he held shut.

"You know I love you more than my own life," she said. "Why punish me? We are all we have. Open up."

In the dark, he reveled in the power he held over the woman behind the door, how he could bring her to her knees, how he could make her beg for his forgiveness as if he could offer sunshine. How he could destroy the both of them. He would kill time to mull over different excuses, what to say, what not, to his mother, if she asked about the bicycle, who could have stolen it. Then, he heard the stomping of soldiers' boots up the stairs, the sound growing harsher, closer. Behind the soldiers, once again, he heard the women's voices rally. They yelped, bickered, rattled like hungry snakes.

If you close your eyes, he thought, you could make everything disappear, or start the world over and give everyone a fresh face. Slowly, his hands slipped away from the doorknob, and he held his breath, wondering what effort it would take to transform into a fish, to exchange his village for the sea.

He blocked out the stampede of the soldiers' boots clanging against the old cedar floor of his room—my God, the noise.

The door flung open. Gunther stood before him breathing hard, his shoulders rocking back and forth. His face shook.

Jean Pierre rose, stood at attention, and began to move his arms in the manner of those British flagmen at sea. Right arm up. Left arm across.

Both arms up. Two arms across. This one at an angle. Both arms down. Now again. Dress rehearsal. Come on, Marcel, are you with me? Those sailors looked so grand and marvelous in their whites, didn't they? For now, he could see no one before him in the room. The effort to perfect those signals cured his weakness to be distracted. Exhausted, he dropped his arms. His face locked into a broad smile. He felt it. He could not control it. A broad, lockjaw smile.

The faces before him blurred. Resembled bubbles actually. And Ssshhh, no one spoke.

He thought of the bicycle thief. He allowed that thought. But only her to enter. That grand Madame from nether parts, careening into the sea, laughing at the empty plates stacked in his bicycle's straw basket, a bicycle he no longer owned; *La vie est pour la vie*, that crazy old woman from Le Nieppe would sing—her blood, the color of orange smiling fish.

Senryu: marina
Elsie O'Day

soft Egyptian sheets
snap in strong October breeze
fair ships-of-the-line

Grand Sable Dunes
Frank J. Hutton

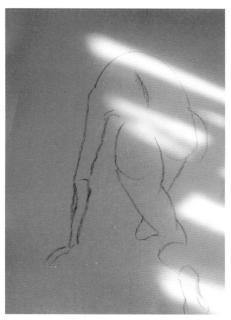

Nude
Sue Haigh

St. George's Day
Cleveland W. Gibson

A STIRRING FEELING GRIPS ME, there is a quickening of pace, I look to the East, to the West to see the splendour, the face of Mankind in unity and hope we all must trust, all linked by will, as the faintest breeze retreats like a ghostly dust. St George's heart ever beats through the land loud and clear. Harken! Listen to the drum; it captures our hope, our deepest dread, and fear. Take heed, in God's splendour, that which never fails to cheer, a rousing shout, when all may quake, because to stand firm, love the free and all of England's dream, hand in hand we walk, my friend. Hoist up, up high that freedom flag, for the love of the red and white, it is a symbol of our hero's blood, spilt for us on a field, against the dragon beast, where the grass will no longer grow.

Where Tectonic Plates Meet
Tiffany Larsen

THE EARTH'S CONTINENTS resemble puzzle pieces. They once fit together to form Pangea; one continent. Magma convected within the mantle. Lava; liquid, molten rock spewed from the mantle as the continental crust diverged and the Pangea drifted apart.

Fresh, dense, rock formed and basins were created. Water, draining from the continents and preexisting oceans into these basins, formed new oceans. This widely accepted theory is called "plate tectonics."

Today, the formation and movement of the earth's crust is a continuous recycling process; forming at mid-oceanic ridges and continent-continent plate boundaries.

When plates converge, the subducting plate returns into the mantle, where it melts and once again becomes magma.

Plate tectonics can destroy whole cities, create super-continents, massive mountain ranges, and generate the enormous power of death and renewal.

Mt. St. Helens

Sunflower
Nick Bakshi

Xyoo Tshiab! (Happy New Year)
Oral Testimony, Neng Xiong

I THINK HMONG CHILDREN born in America can be like lightning: loud and full of risk, but also flash and fresh ideas. The United States is the only home they've ever known. Older children, who remember Laos, now have families. Their memories are filled with helicopters, bombs, and guns and they never want to return. But, I miss the Laos I knew before the war, my people, my farm, the land where I was born.

The world is changing. For this Hmong New Year, I have ancient wishes as the old year is over and the New Year comes. May all good things be yours: prosperity, plentiful food, money, friends, children, health, and peace, everything for everyone! Yes, for this New Year!

Neng Xiong's two sisters from Mailoua, Laos.

Baby Doves
James S. Oppenheim

BIOGRAPHIES

NICK BAKSHI was born in the United States but moved, soon thereafter, to India, where he lived for two years. His father, a native of that country, raised him on internationalism, stressing the importance of world travel and open mindedness. His mother, a former French professor, instilled in him a love for words and language that persists to this day. After spending the last seven months in France, Nick has returned to the United States to finish his studies at Brown University, where he double concentrates in Comparative Literature and Literary Arts. As a freshman, he was awarded the University's Beth Lisa Feldman Prize for his short story: "Little Flowers." His fiction has appeared in *Johnny America, Eclectica Magazine, Elimae, The Forge Journal, Diddledog, Pocket Change,* and *Static Movement.* His greatest aspiration is to one day "out cool" his older sister, Jules, an accomplished dancer and choreographer in New York City.

SITA BHASKAR was born in India and now lives in Madison, Wisconsin. She is the author of *Shielding Her Modesty,* a collection of short stories set on both sides of the globe. Her reviewers mention "Shades of R.K. Narayan." Sita's short stories have been published in *Crab Orchard Review, GSU Review, Desilit Magazine* and *TQR Stories.* She received an Honorable Mention in *Washington Post Magazine's* fiction contest for her story, "Touch of Wrinkled Skin" and placed as a finalist for her story, "Safety in These Times," with the Thomas Wolfe Literary Competition conducted by the North Carolina Writers' Network. She has included this story in the anthology. Set either in India or America or the space in-between where immigrants resist the tug and pull of both sides, Sita calls her stories 'a slice of life.'

ALEX BRAVERMAN was born in Lithuania in 1955, resided in Israel, South Africa, and now lives in Texas. Alex is a mathematician by profession, who finally abandoned this exciting career for the benefit of literature and the art of photography. His stories appeared in publications around the world: USA, Israel, South Africa, Ireland, and India. Alex's photographs are exhibited in New York and

Texas. He is currently working on a book dedicated to photography of modern dance. Our photographic art for the cover was taken by Alex Braverman.

A. JEFFERSON BROWN was born in the United States, a southern boy with a penchant for the darker side of writing. He is a member of Cavender's "Terrible Twelve" with *Horror Library* and has been published in *Our Shadows Speak* and *Dark Distortions*, among others. He is married with two children. Life enjoys him as much as he enjoys it.

RAQUEL CHALFI was born in Tel-Aviv where she lives and works. She studied at Hebrew University, at Berkeley University, and at the American Film Institute. She worked for Israeli radio and television as writer-director/producer, and has taught film at Tel Aviv University. She has published eight volumes of poetry, and is the recipient of numerous awards for her poetry as well as for her work in theater, radio and film. Her collected poems, *Solar Plexus, Poems 1975-1999*, appeared in 2002; in 2006 she received the Bialik Award for poetry as well as the *Israeli Prime Minister's Prize for Hebrew Writers, the Ashman Prize 1999*. Most recently, her work has appeared in the *American Poetry Review, Zoland Annual, Metamorphoses*, and in the anthology: *Poets on the Edge: An Anthology of Contemporary Hebrew Poetry* (SUNY Press, 2008).

Poet Chalfi's translator, **TSIPI KELLER** was born in Prague, raised in Israel, and has been living in the United States since 1974. She is the recipient of several literary awards, including a National Endowment for the Arts Translation Fellowship, CAPS and NYFA awards in fiction, and an Armand G. Erpf award from Columbia University. Her translation of Dan Pagis's posthumous collection, *Last Poems,* was published by *The Quarterly Review of Literature* (1993), and her translation of Irit Katzir's posthumous collection, *And I Wrote Poems*, was published by Carmel, Israel (2000). Her recent translation collections are: *Poets on the Edge An Anthology of Contemporary Hebrew Poetry* (SUNY Press, 2008); and *The Hymns of Job & Other Poems* (BOA Editions, 2008).

L. MCKENNA DONOVAN was born in the United States. She has been an editor, writer and writing coach for eighteen years. Although she works freelance writing for various companies and teaches writing courses on "style" and "creative brainstorming," her current focus is the completion of her Master's in Fine Arts in Creative Writing from Goddard College in Vermont. Her master's thesis is the first volume of a four-volume, cross-genre novel series. While her passion is writing long fiction, she takes occasional breaks to write vignettes in the flash and short story forms. She writes from her home in the Smoky Mountains of western North Carolina.

MARIE LYNAM FITZPATRICK was born in Ireland. She lives and works in the Irish Republic. Marie is a mother and writer. "Under Christian crosses" was reprinted from *The Binnacle,* the University of Maine at Machias, 2006.

MARKO FONG is a fourth generation Chinese-American who was born, raised and lives in Northern California. He never learned to speak Chinese and has never been to China. He recently completed a collection of short stories about the last Chinatown in America, *Inventing China.* It was once one of his dreams to dunk a basketball.

CLEVELAND W. GIBSON was born in colonial India in an atmosphere of color, mystery and intrigue. In the United Kingdom he has worked for many major companies as well as the government. He's been involved with charity work, trained as a Life Guard and was a Road Race Director for over ten years. Since taking up writing he's published over 200 short stories, poems, articles in over eighty-five countries. *Moondust* represents his first surreal book of classic short stories, with a fantasy novel, *Billabongo*, to follow soon. He's married with one son, teaches ESOL, and helps novice writers. Contact him on URL: http://linktiles.com?tile=641

HANNATU GREEN was born in Nigeria and lives in the United States. Hannatu is a born storyteller. She is married with eight children and has been sharing her folk tales with them all her life, as well as the schools and community centers in Minnesota. Hannatu comes from a large extended family with a strong sense of responsibility and a proud African heritage. She noted, "My family were pioneers in everything, the first from my village to embrace western education, medicine and so much more.

JEFF HAAS was born in the United States, received a BA in English Language and Literature from the University of Chicago, and works as a technical writer in Atlanta. He made his first professional sale of a short story called "Cacophony of the Spheres" to *Jim Baen's*

Universe in 2008, and has published over thirty stories online and in print. "Spin Degrees of Freedom," originally published on *Eclectica*, was named a Million Writers Award notable story of the year by *StorySouth*, and "Cacophony of the Spheres" and "Immortality Street" were selected as Editor's Choices by *Bewildering Stories*. Jeff is currently working on a novel called *Sugarville;* a psychological thriller about a man whose faith is tested when he becomes the legal guardian of his troubled nephew.

SUE HAIGH spent most of her life on the north-east coast of Scotland. She now lives and writes deep underground in a cave-house in the Loire valley, France. Stories from her Scottish collection, *The Snow Lazarus*, have been published by Dundee Women and Books (UK), Chistell Publishing, PA (USA), Solander (UK) and *Cadenza Magazine* (UK). "Dreams of Home" was named as a winner in the 2008 *Cadenza Magazine* Open Short Story Competition, under the title of "The Garden." This story was also highly recommended in the "Chapter One Promotions Open International Short Story Competition, 2009." Sue won the Scottish Women's Short Story Competition in 2002, second prize in the 2008 8th Annual Chistell Contest and third prize in the 2008 *Cadenza* competition. Two of her short stories were also short-listed and three long listed in the 2007 *Blinking Eye* competition. Her work has also appeared in Myslexia (UK). She has also written a series of short stories for children, *Stories from a Cave*, set in and around her house in France, as well as two plays for radio. Sue studied in Bristol, Dundee, Paris and Cologne and has worked as a lecturer in languages, a counsellor and a clinical aromatherapist. She is currently working on the final chapters of her novel, *Missing Words*, which is set in Germany and Scotland. This version of "The Dream-Weaver's Son" was workshopped on Zoetrope, as was "Dreams of Home". She is also engaged in research for her next novel, set in medieval Bruges.

ROBERT HAMPTON was born in the United States. Hampton accelerated his work in poetry the past ten years on a work-in-progress; "Ode to An Intelligent Woman." The poetry offered for this anthology is part of that larger work. He's published a few short stories in the seventies and some poetry in the '80s and '90s. He holds an M.A. in English. Robert has scaled down a career in business consulting and communications to special projects. He believes social, economic and political problems may be solved through a creative and artistic strategic and logistical approach instead of through a fragmentary and analytical approach. Hampton's cultural heritage includes Welsh, Scottish, Irish, Bavarian and "according to my mother, Chickasaw Native American. My maternal relatives are Cherokee."

ALAMGIR HASHMI was born in Pakistan. He has published eleven books of poetry and several volumes of literary criticism in the United States, England, Australia, Canada, Pakistan, India and other counties. He has won a number of awards and honors, and his work has been translated into several European and Asian languages. For over three decades he has taught in European, Asian, and U.S. Universities, as Professor of English and Comparative Literature. Although he has little faith in the determinants of birth or death as definitions of cultural life, he cares for people and places. He lived and taught in Cambridge, MA before moving overseas. He has also taught down south and on the West Coast. He began writing at the ripe old age of eleven and has not stopped since. Currently, he lives in Islamabad, Pakistan. © "Kashmir 1987" was reprinted from *Inland and Other Poems* by Alamgir Hashmi (Islamabad: Gulmohar Press, 1988), reprinted here with the author's permission.

KYLE HEMMINGS was born in the United States and holds an MFA in creative writing from National University, California. His stories and poems have been published in *Verb Sap, Insolent Rudder, Night Train, Apple Valley Review, Off-Course Literary Review, Rose and Thorn,* and others. His work gravitates towards the experimental and edgy. Kyle confides his biggest aspiration is to draw like R. Crumb and loves the work of Lynda Barry as well.

FRANK J. HUTTON: Assistant Editor, was born in the United States. Frank is a large format field photographer and fine art printer. His photographic effort centers upon artifacts of cultural history that are vanishing under the rigor of time and the wilderness. His work has been shown in galleries and exhibitions around the Great Lakes. Frank is also an editor of fiction and an author, with essays published in newsprint and works of fiction having appeared in various places, under a variety of pseudonyms. His work can be viewed on the Internet at *handmadeimages.com.*

SHANNA KARELLA was born and raised on a rural Alaskan homestead. Shanna continues to reside in Fairbanks where she makes her living coordinating a social outreach ministry, as a desktop publisher and doing occasional septic system percolation tests. She is a strong advocate of social justice activism and cultural understanding based on the inherent dignity and worth of the human person. Shanna's poetry and essays have been published in print by local press, *Ink Pot* and *The Ester Republic*, as well as online at *Right Hand Pointing* and *The Hiss Quarterly.*

CAPTAIN KATHERINE ELIZABETH KENNEDY (1979-present) was born and raised on a farm in Clear Lake, Iowa. BS: Systems Engineering, West Point, MS: Strategic Intelligence, American Military University. MS: Psychology, Walden University. Katie served in Iraq for two deployments and is deploying fall of 2009 for her third. Katie is writing a book relating to her experiences. She recently left active duty in 2008, currently serving her country in the Army Reserve's Psychological Warfare Group.

TIFFANY LARSEN (1980-present) was born and grew up in the rural community of Clear Lake, Iowa. She graduated from Carleton College, Northfield, MN, in 2003 with a major in geology and from the University of Vermont in 2009, with a Master's of Geology. Tiffany has spent time exploring European cultures through travel and study abroad. She entertains her artistic interests through various media including pottery, painting, and fused glass. She also pursues her passion for sustainable living through organic gardening, and grows produce for local markets.

DEAN LAWSON was born in Canada. He is an English Teacher and lives in Tokyo at the moment with his wife. They are expecting their first child this coming Autumn/09. He has stories and poetry published or forthcoming in *Clockwise Cat, Long Story Short* and other places. Another of his passions is making music. Two songs from his album, *Ballet of the Media,* were used in the film, *Day of the Carp,* a New York International Independent Film winner. "The Palace of Nansi" was reprinted from *Willows Wept Review.*

KULVINDER SINGH MATHARU was born in Tanzania. His parents moved to the UK when he was only two years old. His early childhood revolved around the wonders of science and the beauty of this planet. With his keen interest in electronics, it was only natural he received a bachelor's degree in electrical and electronic engineering and forged a successful career in telecommunications. Now with a steady income, Kulvinder was able to pursue his interests in traveling which, in turn, ignited a dormant need to capture the places he had visited. Initially using an affordable camera with full manual control, he has immersed himself into the world of photography with an on-line photographic portfolio. He provided two photographs: one of a Laotian village and the Mekong River.

ELSIE (STANWOOD) O'DAY was born in the United States and was a native of Maine. She passed away June 17th, 2009. Ms. O'Day authored poetry and short stories. "Rainy Night Swim," appeared in the April edition of *The Linnet's Wings*, two additional poems, "Winter Storm" and "Due North," were published in the fall issue of *Wolf Moon Journal*. She favored disciplined poetry and wrote sonnets, as well as Senryu and prose poetry. She was also working on two novels at the time she passed away.

JAMES S. OPPENHEIM was born in Washington, D.C., raised in Montgomery County, Maryland, schooled in Oxford, Ohio and resident in half a dozen Maryland towns (and, for a summer, Jacksonville, Florida). Jim has published in *Equus, The North American Review, The Washington Post* and *Firehouse Magazine,* and worked as managing editor of the University of Maryland graduate literary magazine, *Ethos.* He has also had a life in music, producing one album and playing venues from cabin porches in West Virginia to bars in Florida. James offered the lovely dove that graces the back of the book. Today finds him in Hagerstown, Maryland as a photographer, singer/songwriter, and the editor of a blog: Oppenheim Arts & Letters (commart.typepad.com) devoted to the understanding of political conflicts and small wars, also art, culture, and language.

AJAY PRASANNAN was born and raised in the UK, where he currently works as a web designer and all-round IT troubleshooter. Regular trips to Kerala allow him to re-connect with his Indian roots and better understand the country he hopes to retire in.

IVAN GABRIEL REHOREK lives in Australia. As he noted, "I was born in the middle of the last century, in the middle of Europe in the middle of a river. That makes me a Gemini Earth Pig Mitsubishi with radiator ascendant, wow. My family is theater people, writers, scientists, musicians and other disturbers of the peace. I breed saxophones (got four already) and on some nights, the moon comes in for a visit.

BILL FRANK ROBINSON was born near Raton, New Mexico. Billy Frank left school in ninth grade to work as a farm laborer. He joined the Air Force in 1950 for four years and spent one year in Korea as a medic in the war zone, three years at Los Angeles County Hospital in the emergency room, thirteen years as a mail carrier, seventeen years as a claims adjudicator for Social Security in San Francisco. He is retired and helping people with income taxes, Medicare, etc. He wrote a monthly serial for *The Voice:* a magazine based in Idaho, for thirty-six episodes. The serial was called "Archie Cleebo."

DIANE P. SMITH, Editor, was born in the United States. Diane retired from child welfare and writes about the homeless, immigrants, the poor, healthcare, those who have little visibility or power in society. She has placed and published in international competition a few times with the *Surrey International Writers Conference* associated with Simon Fraser University, and the *Ottawa Valley Writers' Guild, The Binnacle* at the University of Maine, Machias. She has been honored with fellowships and financial support from the William Wisdom/William Faulkner Society as a finalist in 2005, The Summer Learning Institute through *The Walrus*, and Fish Publishing in Ireland as a finalist for her novel *Balancing Against the Wind.* It remains a work-in-progress.

RALPH SMITH graduated with honors from Rochester Institute of Technology in New York. He offered photographs for the anthology of upstate New York; the photograph for the *Introduction* and Dean Lawson's flash, "Remarkable." He currently works as a freelance photographer in New York City.

RANDY ULLAND granted special permission to use his photographs in this anthology. He said, The work you've seen of Tibet was from my days living and working in East Asia as a journalist. I now live in Oxford, England and most of my time is thinly spread between my family and psychotherapy work. I am, by the way, from Duluth, Minnesota, where most of My family still lives. I went to university in St. Paul.

TOWNSEND WALKER was born in Washington, DC. He now lives in San Francisco after sojourns in New York, Paris, London, and Rome. Townsend has been writing short stories since 2005; a dozen have been published. He has also published books and articles on foreign exchange, derivatives, and portfolio management; the products of a thirty-year career in finance. "Mort pour la France" first appeared in *Raving Dove* and "I Can't Forget" first appeared in *Pequin.*

ANN WALTERS holds a Ph.D. in physical anthropology and was born in the United States. She lives in the Pacific Northwest with her husband and two young daughters. Her poetry has appeared in *Poet Lore, Poetry International, Cadenza, Orbis, The Pedestal Magazine,* and many others. She has been nominated for a *Pushcart Prize* and was short listed for the *2007 LICHEN Tracking,* a Serial Poet competition.

MIKE WOOF was born in Scotland. Mike is a full time journalist living and working in the United Kingdom. He confides he's been to every continent on the planet, barring Antarctica. Mike lived and worked in West Africa for a couple of years and his stories are based on his time there. He mainly travels through Europe and the United States these days. He noted, "A long time ago I was an engineer, but decided I didn't like it. I write as a professional, then get home and write more, mainly fiction. I've got a non-fiction book released."

NENG XIONG was born in Laos. She grew up in a Hmong Village (*Meaung*) and fled to Thailand when her *Meaung* was destroyed in war. She found sanctuary in the United States and became an American citizen. Neng, a widow, lives with her children in Minnesota; two are attending college. Neng's stories are true and stand as testimony to courage and strength.

NOTES

1 Chapter one: *How Beautiful Upon the Hills* comes from *The King James Bible*, Old Testament, Isaiah 52:7, "How beautiful (navu: beautiful) upon the hills are the feet (or footsteps) of Him who declares peace, who announces goodness, who declares salvation."

2 Chapter two: *The Sacred Arunachala* speaks to the Hindu practice of offering aid to those suffering from cancer and stress-related disease. From the URL: indiadivine.org: "Sri Ramana Maharshi (December 30, 1879 April 14, 1950) was a Tamil Saint considered by many to have been a jivanmukta (one who is liberated while still living in their body). He left home for the temple town of Tiruvannamalai at the age of sixteen, and subsequently lived in a cave on the nearby sacred mountain of Arunachala. The following video contains rare archival footage of Sri Ramana Maharshi during his later years."

3 Chapter three: *Say Unto this Mountain* comes from *The King James Bible*, New Testament; Mathew 17:20, "And Jesus said unto them, Because of your unbelief: for verily I say unto you, If ye have faith as a grain of mustard seed, ye shall say unto this mountain, Remove hence to yonder place; and it shall remove; and nothing shall be impossible unto you."

4 Chapter four: *Decisions by Shura*, is taken from *The Qur'an*, text 42:36-38, "…those who believe and put their trust in their Lord; those who avoid the greater sins and indecencies, and when they are angry, even then forgive; those who respond to their Lord, and establish regular prayer; who conduct their affairs by mutual consultation [shura]; who spend out of what We have bestowed on them for sustenance …"

5 Chapter five: *We are as the Mountain* is inspired by Sufi Poet, Rumi. He describes moments of existence in *Sun Of Tabriz*, "We are as the flute, and the music in us is from thee; we are as the mountain and the echo in us is from thee."

6 Chapter Six: *Pilgrimage to Mount Kailish* addresses the fact there is no greater concern than the environment. It touches all of us in every corner of this earth and encompasses all that is. As noted from the URL: http://www.essortment.com/all/mountkailash_rjot.htm "High on the remote western Tibetan plateau, in the northernmost region of the Himalayas, sits Mount Kailash, the holy mountain. The Tibetan people have named it Kang Rinpoche, or Snow Jewel, and the Indians refer to it as Mount Meru. From the URL: essortment. com/all/joutkailash, "Hindu, and Jain pilgrims from the world over go to this holy mountain to circumambulate rather than scale the 22,028 foot high peak. In fact, climbing Mount Kailash is forbidden. The only person to have ever been atop the sacred mountain was Milarepa, a 11th century yogi. Mount Kailash is commonly referred to as the center of the universe in Eastern religious texts from India to Japan. Rooted in the seventh hell and bursting through the highest heaven, it is also believed to be the World Pillar."

7 Chapter seven: *Justice Hung in the Balance* addresses war. The Humanists' Views; From the URL: ppu.org.uk/learn/infordocs/ st_religions note "In recent times religion has played a decreasing role in many societies, particularly in the West. Many people have consciously rejected the notion of a spiritual and sacred religion or God. This does not necessarily mean the rejection of ethical principles. Some people have developed a philosophy of 'humanism'. This is based on humanitarian ideals, such as individual responsibility for one's actions and respect for others."

8 Chapter eight: *Piacere Rubato: Stolen Pleasure* is dedicated to love and nonsense.

9 Poet Raquel Chalfi has eleven books published in her name. She often leaves spaces in her poetry that address the pregnant pauses in life, death and so much more. She has been honored with several awards for poetry.

10 Neng Xiong has shared her stories with the editor and her words have been enhanced with a poetic slant. Neng's life stands as testimony to courage and strength.

11 Andrew McIntosh Patrick and his sister, Ann Patrick, granted special permission to reproduce, *A City Garden* for our first edition.

12 http://en.wikipedia.org/wiki/File:Fort_knox_maine_painting.jpg it was noted: "Seth Eastman's painting [Fort Knox, Maine] is in the public domain in the United States because it is a work of the United States Federal Government under the terms of Title 17, Chapter 1, Section 105 of the US Code. See Copyright."

13 Randy Ulland granted special permission to use his photographs in this anthology. He said, "The work you've seen of Tibet was from my days living and working in East Asia as a journalist. I now live in Oxford, England and most of my time is thinly spread between my family and psychotherapy work. I am, by the way, from Duluth, MN, where most of my family still lives. I went to university in St. Paul."